STORIES
TO HOLD AN
AUDIENCE

STORIES
TO HOLD AN
AUDIENCE

CATHERINE HAMMOND

**MILLENNIUM
BOOKS**

First published in 1994 by
Millennium Books
an imprint of E.J. Dwyer (Australia) Pty Ltd
3/32-72 Alice Street
Newtown NSW 2042
Australia
Phone: (02) 550-2355
Fax: (02) 519-3218

National Library of Australia
Cataloguing-in-Publication data

Hammond, Catherine.
  Stories to hold an audience.

  Includes index.
  ISBN 1 86429 005 6.

  1. Anecdotes. I. Title.

808.88

Cover design by Megan Smith
Text design by Megan Smith
Typeset in New Baskerville 10/13 pt by Post Typesetters
Printed in Australia by McPherson's Printing Group

10 9 8 7 6 5 4 3 2 1
97 96 95 94

INTRODUCTION

A good story has a life of its own. It will be used in different ways. It will say different things to different people. No one can accurately predict its effect on an audience, or on any member in it.

The fastest way to spoil a good story is to start talking about its "moral" or theme. So why are we listing themes for the stories in this book? The list is only meant to help speakers, teachers, leaders and preachers find stories that could be appropriate for their chosen topic. Needless to say, any of the stories might be considered relevant to many more themes than are suggested here.

A word about the quotations: they were chosen to expand or enhance—or radically change—our experience of the stories. Every quotation was selected for that reason and not for its author.

One final point: even though the wording of some of the quotations is not inclusive, it was retained as originally written, out of respect for the historical source.

The universe is made of stories, not of atoms.
MURIEL RUKEYSER

Anyone may tell a story, and if it is an absorbing one,
someone will listen.
HALLIE BURNETT

CONTENTS

....

CHAPTERS AND THEMES

THEME INDEX

A Fable for Storytellers

The members of a certain club knew they had to do something to bring new life to their organization or it would soon fold. They were a unique group in that their whole purpose was to promote storytelling as a path to wisdom.

After much discussion they decided to send two of the brightest of their members to a special workshop designed to help people think creatively.

The two women chosen were Freida Full and Emily Empty. At the club's first meeting following the workshop, Freida and Emily gave their reports. Freida said she had found nothing really new or helpful at all. In fact, just as she had predicted, she had heard it all before.

Emily's report was very different. For fifteen minutes she outlined for the group several possible strategies they might try to reinvigorate their program and entice new members. She was quite optimistic about their chances.

"Why such a difference in these two reports?" one member wanted to know. Freida Full started to say something as did Emily Empty, but before they could, the president emeritus said: "We are a storytelling club, so may I offer a fable in reply?" When the others nodded, he said:

"Two little jugs went to the fountain to get water for their thirsty garden plants. But one was already full of odds and ends collected here and there. Only the empty one had room for the fountain's fresh, clear water. Only she could bring drink for the withered plants."

The sure way to miss success is to miss the opportunity.
PHILARETE CHASLES

*[Optimism]: that very popular trust in flat
things coming round!*
CHARLES DICKENS

*Opportunities are usually disguised as hard work,
so most people don't recognise them.*
ANN LANDERS

The true art of memory is the art of attention.
SAMUEL JOHNSON

THEMES
■ WISDOM ■ OPTIMISM
■ VANITY ■ OPENNESS

Between the Slats

A boy decided to build a new railing for the front verandah of his
house. Unfortunately he was not a good repairer and when he poked
his head between two slats to hammer in a nail, he found he could not
get his head out again!

Poor boy! He called out to neighbors and passersby, but everyone burst out laughing when they saw him and did nothing to help.
He was a member of an ethnic minority in those parts and so to see
him in such a sad situation actually delighted some!

"Hey there, John," they cried. "What are you doing in the cage?
Won't the keeper let you out? Ha! Ha!"

And so it went for almost an hour. When a group of young men
came back for a second time an old carpenter, well known in the
town, happened on the scene. The noisy group caught sight of the
poor boy still with his head between the slats. "What kind of animal
is that?" one called out to the others with mocking sarcasm.

The carpenter grasped the whole situation in a second. "The animals," he shouted, "are already on parade on this street. In fact, you're all too cruel to be animals!"

So saying, he marched up onto the verandah and set the boy free.

Hain't we got all the fools in town on our side?
And ain't that a big enough majority in any town?
MARK TWAIN

All animals are equal, but some animals are
more equal than others.
GEORGE ORWELL

A hurtful act is the transference to others of the
degradation which we bear in ourselves.
SIMONE WEIL

THEMES
▪ PREJUDICE ▪ COMPASSION
▪ RACISM ▪ KINDNESS ▪ EQUALITY

No-Nut

Three ducklings became lost on a small lake near the bush. Their names were Hi-Tech, E-Motional and No-Nut. Hi-Tech approached their problem very rationally. She was a clever duck and had brought her mobile phone and CB radio with her when the three had started out.

"Never fear!" she told her brothers. "I'll get us out of here in no time." But all her efforts to raise help failed. Their location was out of range for both the phone and the radio.

As night came on, E-Motional lived up to his name and cried buckets while somehow managing to wail piteously at the same time. It was sunrise before he and Hi-Tech swam into some reeds and fell into a troubled sleep, exhausted from their night's activities and worry.

The third duckling, No-Nut, had slept calmly all night despite the moans and sobs nearby. Unlike the others, he hadn't appeared too upset by their problem. ("Too stupid," his brother and sister had murmured on the side. "Really knows nothing—doesn't even realise the danger we're in!")

When morning came, No-Nut stretched lazily, stifled a yawn, wiggled his feet and paddled out onto the lake. Little though he was, the confident duckling made a ripple as he swam. The ripple spread further and further out as ripples always do.

Overhead an anxious wild duck spotted the ripple and zeroed in. "No-Nut!" she honked in glad recognition. "Stay where you are. I'll come to get you."

No-Nut swam back to the shore, as placidly as he had swum out. "Hey you two," he called to his brother and sister. "We're not lost any more. Mother's coming for us."

The other two looked in amazement at their "stupid" brother. They seemed more angry than happy to be saved. After all, it was humiliating to have No-Nut as a savior. He wasn't the type—you know, no brains, no charisma, no ability to ponder matters carefully . . . He didn't even have the sense to be properly frightened!

"But that's just the point," said their mother later. "You're all safe now because No-Nut had enough trust to carry on naturally: Sleep, swim and... make a ripple!"

The shortest answer is doing.
LORD HERBERT

What a man believes may be ascertained not from his creed, but from the assumptions on which he habitually acts.
GEORGE BERNARD SHAW

Deliberation is the work of many. Action, of one alone.
CHARLES DE GAULLE

One of the conclusions I have come to in my old age is the importance of living in the ever-present now.
RUTH CASEY

THEMES
■ EMOTION ■ TECHNOLOGY ■ CALM
■ TRUST ■ CONFIDENCE ■ ACTION

Two of a Kind

A certain woman became famous both for her music and her personal story of hardship and bravery. Everything she did was successful.

One day she decided to renovate her lovely old summer home in the country, giving special attention to the kitchen.

The village tradesperson she called in to do the job was a man of few words, like most folks in that area. The grand lady, on the contrary, always seemed to be on the stage, even in the kitchen. Moreover, she had so successfully directed all the events in her life and the lives of her husband and children that she couldn't stop directing everyone everywhere.

Each time she went to check on how the carpenter was doing, she would have a critical comment to make. "This corner is not rounded enough... This benchtop is not smooth enough... This cupboard is not deep enough..." And so it went, day after day. What the carpenter accomplished in one afternoon usually had to be redone after the next day's visit from the woman.

Finally the exasperated man could stand it no longer. "Lady," he said before she could start her criticisms for the day, "I've just realised that you and I are exactly alike."

"Hardly!" she snorted indignantly as if to say: "Compared to what I've done in my life, what could you and I possibly have in common?"

But the villager continued doggedly: "People say that the whole world's your stage and when you're on, there's no room for anyone else. Just like me, I say. Every job I do is my stage and when I'm on, there's no room for anyone else. So off you go madam, and don't come back 'til I'm done." He then proceeded to finish the kitchen to perfection.

Nothing is more unpleasant than a virtuous
person with a mean mind.
WALTER BAGEHOT

I don't mind how much my ministers talk,
as long as they do what I say.
MARGARET THATCHER

Power admits no equal.
EDWARD MOORE

The really great man is the one who makes
everyone feel great.
G. K. CHESTERTON

THEMES
■ EXPERTISE ■ SKILL ■ CRITICISM
■ COMPETENCE ■ BOSSINESS

The Protester

She was somewhat of a rebel from a well-known family. She liked nothing more than to be closeted in a garret in one of the university town's old houses, busily putting together projects and newsletters for some cause or other.

Long ago she had written off her father as a "typically stodgy professor" of sociology, always buried in his books.

"Harsh words, my girl, about your old Dad," was his only comment. Friends of the family felt it was a pity that the father and daughter had grown increasingly further apart. She was unaware that he was gradually becoming somewhat of an expert on international relations and in demand for various speaking engagements. All she knew was that he was going on more and more overseas trips. "What a life of luxury!" she remarked sarcastically. "He flits around while the environment is being despoiled and the poor are getting poorer. At least I'm trying to do something to help."

Marches were not for her. She could give talks, write news releases, lobby for her causes... but not march or join any public protests. It was a deep-rooted fear of exposure to ridicule—something she ruefully acknowledged she must have inherited from her very proper, proud father. Hadn't he drilled it into her that "public displays were vulgar"? The most she could do was cheer the marchers from the sidelines.

That was where she was on the day of the anti-nuclear march—the first one in a town situated near a uranium mine that generated most of the region's income. To her disappointment the marchers were very few. It would surely all be dismissed by the papers as a failure: "the usual crowd of young people who turn up for any protest." There were no older or prominent townspeople among them...

That is, until she saw her father! He was walking quietly along with his usual dignity, head high, step firm. He carried no placard but his conviction about nuclear weapons was written all over him.

That was the day she lost one fear and acquired another. She found that conviction can overcome the fear of being humiliated and she learned to fear her own self-assured judgment of others. It was the day she grew up.

"Dad!" she cried and swung into the march beside him.

*To sin by silence when they should protest
makes cowards out of men.*
ABRAHAM LINCOLN

Even the youngest of us may be wrong sometimes.
GEORGE BERNARD SHAW

*[People] may rise on stepping stones
Of their dead selves to higher things.*
ALFRED LORD TENNYSON

My life has been a tapestry of rich and royal hue,
An everlasting vision of the ever-changing view.
CAROLE KING

THEMES
■ COURAGE ■ JUDGMENT ■ ACTION
■ PROTEST ■ UNDERSTANDING ■ MATURITY

On the Tightrope

To Tony the Tightrope Walker the space between two tall buildings held an almost irresistible attraction. He would at once picture a rope stretched between them and himself balanced on it, high above the street—which of course would be packed with admiring crowds all straining upwards, eyes fixed on him.

As a tightrope performer, Tony had one success after another and soon his fame grew. Then one day, in the heat of an argument, a man whom he considered a friend yelled: "You know, you're not as clever as you make out. You're really scared to death because you know you've just been lucky. You know you're not really a world-class performer!"

After that Tony practiced more than ever, striving with everything he had to improve his technique. In fact, soon he practiced more and more and performed less and less. Finally he was hardly giving any performances at all.

"Everything's fine while I'm practicing," he confided in desperation to a wise old uncle who had come to visit him. "But lately when I get up on the high wire, everything starts going wrong. I almost feel a fall coming on."

This old uncle had heard about the former friend's remarks and the change that had come over the performer since. "Tony," he said, "you're wrong when you say you feel a fall coming on. You've already fallen before you even leave the ground. Until you heal that fall from self-confidence, you'll never make it on the rope—or in life."

The heart of the wise, like a mirror, should reflect all objects without being sullied by any.
CONFUCIUS

We see things not as they are, but as we are.
H. M. TOMLINSON

The only thing we have to fear is fear itself.
FRANKLIN ROOSEVELT

There are hazards in anything one does, but there are greater hazards in doing nothing.
SHIRLEY WILLIAMS

THEMES
■ **CONFIDENCE** ■ **BELIEF**
■ **SELF-KNOWLEDGE** ■ **CRITICISM**

The Master's Reply

If a Zen Master were telling the Gospel story of Martha and Mary, it might go something like this:

One day Jesus came to the house of Lazarus and his two sisters, Martha and Mary. Mary seated herself at the Master's feet and eagerly took in every word he said. She was utterly lost in contemplating his expressions, his gestures, his whole manner as he spoke words of great truth and love.

Martha was busily preparing a delicious meal for her distinguished guest and his disciples. At first she worked away happily, thrilled at the honor that had come to her house that day. But after a while, she began to fuss and fret because so much needed to be done quickly and she was all alone in the kitchen. "Why isn't Mary here helping me?" she muttered under her breath. As she grew more upset, everything she needed seemed to be hiding from her.

She couldn't find her favorite bowl. She couldn't find her sharpest knife. Finally she stormed out of the kitchen on a furious search of Mary.

When Jesus saw her red, flushed face, he suppressed a smile and asked gently, "What is the matter?"

"I'm looking for my sister!" said Martha, embarrassed at how flustered she must look.

"Looking for your sister?" repeated the Master. "No, Martha is looking for Martha."

Our characters are the result of our conduct.
ARISTOTLE

Heaven must be in me before I can be in heaven.
CHARLES STANFORD

*It is the quality of our work which will please
God and not the quantity.*

MAHATMA GANDHI

*When one is a stranger to oneself, then one is
estranged from others too.*

ANNE MORROW LINDBERGH

THEMES
■ SEARCHING ■ SELF-POSSESSION
■ ANGER ■ SELF-KNOWLEDGE

Philosophy in Action

The famous philosopher Socrates was one scholar who really
approached life philosophically. From all reports, his wife Xantippe
was of quite a different temperament. Her husband's love of discussion and his method of imparting wisdom through dialogue actually
often exasperated her. She obviously thought he should change his
ways and use his time more wisely (which is quite funny when you
consider that Socratic wisdom has been a byword for more than two
thousand years).

Anyway, the story goes that Socrates was holding a discussion at
the front of his house. Xantippe was bustling about inside and
grumbling as usual about her "useless" husband. Undisturbed, he let
her carry on. Finally she opened an upstairs window and dumped a
bucket of water down on the hapless Socrates.

Still unperturbed, the philosopher remarked, "That was to be
expected. After so much thunder you're bound to get some rain!"

To teach the wisdom of accepting people as we find them is a
great service. To live that teaching when the storm rages is even
greater.

The narrower the mind, the broader the statement.
PROCTOR FYFFE COOK

Anger is a brief madness.
HORACE

The flour is the important thing, not the mill;
the fruits of philosophy, not the philosophy itself.
G. C. LICHTENBERG

THEMES
▪ CALM ▪ ANGER
▪ WISDOM ▪ PHILOSOPHY

Which One?

It's always a surprise to discover that someone you thought you knew well has quite a different view of things...

Mick the Irishman had married the girl of his dreams, Molly, his sweet Irish rose.

As they proceeded down the aisle after the ceremony, he turned to her with a happy smile.

"Isn't it grand, Molly—now we are one!"

Quick as a flash the lass replied, "Yes, Mick, and *I'm* the one!"

*Infantile love follows the principle: I love because
I am loved. Mature love follows the principle:
I am loved because I love.*
ERICH FROMM

It takes two to tango.
SONG TITLE, HOFFMAN AND MANNING

If two ride on a horse, one must ride behind.
SHAKESPEARE

*Secretly, we wish anyone we love will think
exactly the way we do.*
KIM CHERNIN

THEMES
■ MARRIAGE ■ UNITY
■ OPINIONS ■ LOVE

The Healing Interest

The nurses in a certain ward were all fond of one elderly patient because he never made a fuss, no matter what painful treatment he had to undergo or what discomfort he felt. To every request and every directive from the doctor he always acquiesced patiently.

"What an easy man to take care of!" was the usual comment from the staff.

"That may be," thought one doctor, "but it looks to me as if our dear old friend is so submissive because he really has no interest in living. One of these days he'll just quietly turn over and die if something doesn't happen to put some life into him!"

So the doctor made an effort to try to discover some hobby or interest that would do the trick. "No, doctor," the patient responded to each question. "I've never had time to do anything for fun. I haven't got any special interests or talents. Only ever read the paper when I had a spare moment."

But the kindly doctor persisted and eventually it turned out that the patient had a yearning to try making clay figures—droll yet lovable characters, each with a distinct personality. He had no idea whether he could actually do it but just the thought of trying brought a light to his eyes.

Some clay was brought in—only a small kit at first— and before long the old man had produced his first figurine, and then another . . . and another . . .

He proved to be quite skilled at it and soon a businessman was found who took interest in the figurines as a commercial venture. The old man now had no thought but his newfound love. He began to be annoyed when he was interrupted by doctors and nurses while he was modelling. Sketches, hunks of clay and half-finished figures were everywhere in his corner of the ward. He had become the most active patient of all. "Not at all easy to handle any more," one nurse remarked.

But the fact was that without hardly anyone realising it, least of all the old man himself, he was getting stronger and healthier every day. Finally, not only was he no longer a "good patient"—he wasn't a patient at all.

There is nothing impossible in all the world except that the human heart is wanting in resolution.
CONFUCIUS

Nothing is unthinkable, nothing is impossible to the balanced person, provided it arises out of the needs of life and is dedicated to life's further development.
LEWIS MUMFORD

Let us live while we live.
PHILIP DODDRIDGE

Each of us lives each day with special gifts which are a part of our very being, and life is a process of discovering and developing these God-given gifts within each one of us.
JEANE DIXON

THEMES
■ HEALING ■ WILL TO LIVE
■ CREATIVITY ■ KINDNESS ■ LIFE

What Changed?

It was my first trip home to my country town after a few years of living in New York City. I had a copy in my mind of every street and building in that little town and I expected to just lay it right down, perfect fit, as I drove in. Before I had left home to try my luck in the Big Apple, I had a habit of blowing things way out of proportion, making them "bigger than life," to use my mother's words. A few years living among some fifteen million people had done a lot to make me more realistic in my outlook, I was sure. Now, I felt I could see life as it really was.

But by the time I had driven through town, pulled up in front of the old house and greeted the family, I was in a mild state of shock.

"How does the old place look to you?" my mother was asking.

"It's the same but it all seems so small!" I spluttered, trying to find the right words. "I mean, as I drove up Hill Street, it didn't seem to be a big hill at all, and the Town Hall is much smaller than I remember it. And our house, it's like a miniature of the house I remember—these steps up to the verandah look so small and fragile! It's like I've come to a doll's house—everything seems to have shrunk!"

My mother was silent only for a moment. "It's not the town that's different," she said slowly. "You are."

It was then that I gained some understanding of the old saying, "You can't stand in the same river twice."

The difference is no less real because it is of degree.
BENJAMIN CARDOZA

Things do not change; we change.
HENRY DAVID THOREAU

People themselves alter so much that there is
something new to be observed in them for ever.
JANE AUSTEN

THEMES
■ PERSPECTIVE
■ EXPERIENCE ■ REALITY

The Choice

The story is told of a great Japanese swordsman named Tsukahara who had three sons. All three had acquired their father's superb skill in fencing, so when it came time to appoint one as his successor, Tsukahara devised a test.

The old man's test, however, was not just one of skill. He was looking to see which son had the maturity required.

Accordingly, he rigged a ball over the doorway to his room in such a way that when his sons entered, it would topple down. Then he called his youngest son.

As the youth entered, the ball started to drop, but his reflexes were so quick that he had drawn his sword and sliced it in two before it reached him. Despite this brilliant effort, the father's reaction was one of strong displeasure.

The second son caught the ball in his hands. Afterwards, like his brother before him, he was asked to wait in his room.

The oldest son had barely started to enter the room when he sensed that something was amiss. Looking up, he saw the ball precariously perched above him and took it down. "You wanted me, Father?" he asked.

In announcing his decision to make the oldest son his successor, Tsukahara reproved the youngest for excitedly slicing the ball, telling him he wanted to see more control. To the second son he was encouraging, telling him to grow even more reflective. The third, he said, had the maturity needed: to be a master swordsman you must become one who does not need the swordsman's skills.

If your aim is control, it must be self-control first.
ANONYMOUS

Experience is not what happens to a man. It is what a man does with what happens to him.
ALDOUS HUXLEY

At twenty years of age, the will reigns; at thirty, the wit; and at forty, the judgment.
HENRY GRATTAN

You gain strength, courage, and confidence by every experience by which you really stop to look fear in the face.
ELEANOR ROOSEVELT

THEMES
■ INTUITION ■ CONTROL ■ REACTION
■ MATURITY ■ EXPERIENCE

Head in the Clouds

The famed German philosopher Edith Stein, who became a Carmelite nun known as Sr Benedicta, was a prisoner of the Nazis in the camp of Westerbork. Her next stop would be Auschwitz and an ignominious death for the sole reason that she was Jewish.

Edith had been a scholar, an assistant to the renowned philosopher Husserl, a popular lecturer, and a writer. She had become a convert to Catholicism after reading the autobiography of St Teresa of Avila and, twelve years after her baptism, had entered a Carmelite monastery. But unlike the great Teresa, the Foundress of her Order, Edith Stein was not known for practicality or common sense. She was in fact the proverbially impractical scholar. How would she cope in the horrifying conditions of a concentration camp where even the most clever and inventive types had given up hope?

Edith had always been so intent on scholarly pursuits, on getting at the deepest meaning underlying all reality, that she had developed few domestic skills. Indeed, her attempts at sewing and cleaning in the convent had been remarkably unsuccessful! Even simply carrying a statue in a procession had sealed her reputation for having her "head in the clouds": she had hit an overhead oil lamp with the head of St Joseph and when the oil came pouring down on her, instead of getting out of the way as fast as possible, Edith had stood stock still and tried to figure out why she was being showered with oil!

Now here was this impractical scholar a prisoner of ruthless enemies! As intelligent as she was, she surely recognised the utter hopelessness of their situation. One would have expected her to be incapable of doing anything practical or beneficial for herself.

Yet the amazing fact, testified to by survivors, is that this very same Sr. Benedicta not only showed a calm presence of mind throughout the ordeal, but it was she, not their distraught mothers, who took care of the needs of the many frightened and neglected children. How was she able to do this? Only she of all the prisoners had left the past and the future in God's hands and was living in the now. So only she was open to the real needs of the moment. Perhaps it was then and there that Edith Stein showed herself to be a true philosopher.

There are people who... accept whatever happens day to day without struggle or question or regret. To them things just are, like the earth and sky and seasons.
CELESTE DE BLASIS

I shall never believe that God plays dice with the world.
ALBERT EINSTEIN

I have read somewhere or other... that history is philosophy teaching by examples.
HENRY ST JOHN BOLINGBROKE

Every situation—nay, every moment—is of infinite worth; for it is the representative of a whole eternity.
WOLFGANG VON GOETHE

THEMES
■ ACCEPTANCE ■ PRACTICALITY ■ SERENITY
■ PHILOSOPHY ■ KINDNESS ■ GOD
■ RELIGION ■ HOLINESS

Dilemma

Suppose your sister wrote home on a visit to New York City to tell you about an absolutely incredible experience. She and a date went up to the observation deck of the Empire State Building to take in the spectacular view. While there, the fellow lifted up her chin and bent down for a little kiss.

Wham! According to your sister, something utterly amazing happened! The letter says: "Believe me, I know what you must be thinking but I mean it literally when I say that we got a shock! An actual electric shock went through both of us as soon as our lips touched. It was the most mind-boggling experience I've ever had! I've always believed that I would know it when the real thing came along, but I never expected it to be so dramatic as this!"

And on and on the letter goes. In short, your sister is now totally in love and what had started out as a casual date has blossomed into a full-blown romantic involvement.

You are happy for her, especially as the letters begin to show signs of a deepening and very fulfilling relationship. Just before the letter announcing the engagement arrives, you happen to see an item in the paper about the Empire State Building. To your astonishment it speaks about the unusual fact that from the 86th floor up, given certain atmospheric conditions, a kiss can give an electric shock!

What would you decide to do: Tell your sister? Or say nothing to anyone?

It is only in literature that coincidences seem unnatural.
ROBERT LYND

*Most of us love from our need to love, not because
we find someone deserving.*
NIKKI GIOVANNI

The story of a love is not important—what is important is that one is capable of love. It is perhaps the only glimpse we are permitted of eternity.

HELEN HAYES

All chance [is] direction which thou canst not see.

ALEXANDER POPE

THEMES

▪ **COINCIDENCE** ▪ **TRUE LOVE** ▪ **DECISIONS**

A Revelation

A couple had five sons and over the years, as relatives and friends visited their home, the mother had gotten into the habit of introducing her boys in order of age.

"This is my number one son," she would say, "my oldest. And this is number two son, who is going into high school this year." And so she would go on down the line. Usually the kids were dragged away from play or studies or whatever they were doing to be brought into the lounge and duly introduced.

Both parents were given to boasting about their sons and predicting their futures. "Our number three son here is a whiz at football—he'll make the sports pages some day." And so it went.

One night when their mother called up the stairs for the boys to come down and be introduced to her old school friends, the four oldest reluctantly trooped down, but Peter, the five-year-old, dreading another session, called down in a voice loud enough to be heard by all: "I'm busy. Can't you just give them my number?"

And suddenly the other four children knew why they had always resented the introduction routine...

*A child develops individuality long
before he develops taste.*
ERMA BOMBECK

*To be nobody but myself, in a world which is doing its
best night and day to make me everybody else, means to
fight the hardest battle which any human being can fight
and never stop fighting.*
E. E. CUMMINGS

*We know what a person thinks not when he tells
us what he thinks but by his actions.*
BASHEVIS SINGER

THEMES
■ INDIVIDUALITY ■ INSENSITIVITY
■ UNIQUENESS ■ SELF-EXPRESSION

Through Their Eyes

It was Christmas time again and the teacher asked her little ones to draw the usual picture of Jesus in the manger. Throughout the weeks leading up to this last class before Christmas, she had been trying to impress upon the children that Jesus was a normal human baby just as they had been, and that he was part of family life too, just as they were.

When the class had finished the project, they were asked to hang their drawings up around the room. The teacher went around to admire each one and to talk with its creator about it. Good teacher that she was, she refrained from giving any interpretation of the paintings so that the children would spontaneously interpret them for her themselves.

When one particular boy had finished explaining his drawing, she realised that he had not mentioned a feminine figure behind Mary and Joseph in the stable.

"And who is this?" she asked brightly.

His answer was matter-of-fact: "Her? Oh, that's the baby-sitter!"

To be a child: it is to have a spirit yet streaming from the waters of baptism; it is to believe in love, to believe in loveliness, to believe in belief.
FRANCIS THOMPSON

My reverence has always been for holy simplicity rather than wordy vulgarity.
ST JEROME

It's innocence when it charms us,
ignorance when it doesn't.
MIGNON McLAUGHLIN

THEMES
▪ CHILDREN ▪ INNOCENCE
▪ SIMPLICITY ▪ PRACTICALITY

What's-His-Name Now

They lived on a small farm on the outskirts of a country town. As the three boys in the family grew up, it was obvious that the farm could not support them and each in turn found other work.

The oldest—"tall, broad-shouldered Tom," "Tom with the dark wavy hair"—found work in a foundry and soon became known throughout the area for his tremendous capacity for hard work, his love of a good time, his ability to hold his grog (and great quantities of it), his good looks and way with women (especially on the dance floor).

Bill, the second son, worked in the town's only factory. As tall as his brother, he was a bit thinner but what he lacked in muscle he made up in aggressiveness. He too was a good looker and a good dancer but his Saturday nights usually ended in rousing fights.

The youngest son Frank seemed to have come from a different family altogether. He was short and puny, with a chest left slightly caved in from a childhood bout of rickets. No matter how hard he tried (and his one ambition was to be like his brothers) he could not do anything they did. His physical strength was practically non-existent, any alcoholic drink made him sick, and he was painfully shy with girls.

When people spoke about the family, they invariably said something like, "Tom, Bill and . . . what's-his-name?"

Years later, when Frank spoke of his youth, he would talk quite openly about the difference between him and his two brothers. "You don't seem to carry any scars from the experience of those years," someone once commented. "In fact, you went on to distinguish yourself at university and then in a career in education. Where did you get a sense of your own worth?"

Without hesitation, Frank replied: "From my mother. It saddened her to see me so upset about being short, thin, and so lacking in everything my brothers had. She couldn't comfort me until one day something she said really got through to me and I was okay from then on."

Frank paused, remembering. "She took me aside, squared me around to look right at her, and then said emphatically, 'It's not how high your shoulders are from the ground that counts—it's what's above them!'"

If you think you can, you are right;
"If you think you can't, you are right.
HENRY LORD

To believe in something not yet proved and to
underwrite it with our lives; it is the only way we
can leave the future open.
LILLIAN SMITH

God does not ask about your ability—
only about your availability.
ANONYMOUS

Attitudes are contagious.
ENGLISH PROVERB

THEMES
■ SELF-ESTEEM ■ ATTITUDE
■ AFFIRMATION ■ ENCOURAGEMENT
■ INDIVIDUALITY ■ BELIEF

The New Factor

A certain college professor was known for his extremely liberal views. He particularly railed against what he called "old phobias" about sex and sexual relationships. "Everything should be open and uninhibited. Young men and women need to experiment with sex," he would proclaim at every chance he had.

One of his students returned to the college some years later and decided to look him up. Class was in session when the former student arrived, so he took a seat quietly in the back of the room. He hadn't been there very long before he realised that there had been a radical change in the professor's thinking.

In fact, the student found his former lecturer's ideas were completely different, especially on the topic of women, and men's attitudes and practices in relation to women.

Afterwards, he couldn't help but remark, "You've certainly changed. What happened since I last saw you?"

Without hesitation the professor replied, "I've now got a daughter."

It seems to me that since I've had children,
I've grown richer and deeper.
ANNE TYLER

The reproduction of mankind is a great marvel and
mystery. Had God consulted me in the matter, I should
have advised him to continue the generation of the
species by fashioning them of clay.
MARTIN LUTHER

Sex itself must always, it seems to me, come to us
as a sacrament and be so used or it is meaningless.
The flesh is suffused by the spirit, and it is
forgetting this in the act of lovemaking that
creates cynicism and despair.
MAY SARTON

THEMES
■ **SEX** ■ **ATTITUDE** ■ **RELATIONSHIPS**
■ **PERSPECTIVE** ■ **CHILDREN**
■ **OPINIONS** ■ **EXPERIENCE**

Reassurance

The four-year-old girl was obviously frightened: what she had just heard from the TV preacher about the devil going around seeking people to attack was the stuff of nightmares!

As usual she went to her big brother for comfort. Though only two years older, he seemed very wise to her. "I'm scared of this devil guy," she whimpered.

"Oh forget it," he soothed. "Don't you remember how we found out about Santa Claus? This devil guy will probably turn out to be Dad too!"

It is a wise child who knows its own father.
ENGLISH PROVERB

One cannot have wisdom without living life.
DOROTHY McCALL

Experience is the father of wisdom.

ENGLISH PROVERB

Children begin by loving their parents.
After a while, they judge them. Rarely, if ever,
do they forgive them.

OSCAR WILDE

THEMES
■ EXPERIENCE ■ CHILDREN
■ DISCOVERY ■ DEVIL

The Power of Tradition

The young husband obviously loved to cook and the dinners he served his new wife convinced her that she was indeed a lucky woman.

One thing puzzled her, though, and at last she decided to enquire. "Darling, why do you always cut a small piece off the end of the roast before you put it into the oven?"

"Well," he replied, "to tell the truth, I do it because my mother always does it."

At the next family gathering, the wife decided to satisfy her curiosity. She drew her mother-in-law aside and put the question to her. The older woman went a bit red, and replied, "Well, to tell the truth, I do it because my mother always does it."

Undaunted, the wife waited until they paid a visit to eighty-five-year-old Nan. Knowing she'd enjoy hearing the story, she told her about her persevering quest to find the answer to the chopped-off roast.

"Struth!" she croaked. "Imagine the two of them doing that! Why, I only cut the piece off because my pan was too small!"

Traditions are the guideposts driven deep into our subconscious minds. The most powerful ones are those we can't even describe, aren't even aware of.
ELLEN GOODMAN

There was never anything... so well devised... which in continuance of time has not been corrupted.
BOOK OF COMMON PRAYER

Without the aid of custom, I should not be able to find my way across the room.
WILLIAM HAZLITT

THEMES
■ TRADITION ■ ADAPTABILITY ■ CUSTOM

The Second Ride

Johnny and Karen had been good friends all through their school years and afterwards. They had similar interests and did a lot of things together, although they always said that "they were just very good friends... nothing more." That's the way it was.

When they each reached their 21st birthdays—just a month apart—they decided to celebrate the big event together. All their friends came and the party was a huge success. Johnny's closest friend got the idea of making up an engagement story to have a little fun with Johnny and Karen. The rumor made the rounds and at the 21st everyone was waiting for the "big announcement."

When the joke came out, Johnny and Karen laughed harder than the rest, enjoying the fun. But in the weeks that followed, parents and friends began to put gentle pressure on the two to think seriously about their relationship. "You two are made for each other," people said. "Don't you realize what you mean to each other?"

The upshot of it all was that a year later, Johnny and Karen were married. The wedding was the social event of the year in their country town. Everyone joined in with decorating both the car and the reception hall. The car's big sign read: "Just Married—Best Friends!"

The marriage, however, was a disaster right from the start, despite the couple's best efforts. "We were fine as friends," they realized. "We should never have let them talk us into this."

Divorce seemed the only answer. The final papers came through a few days before Karen was due to leave town for a new job. Johnny, too, was starting a new life elsewhere.

Honest as they had always been, they admitted to each other that the one person each would miss the most was the other. That's when Johnny got an idea...

A few hours later, a white Jag drove slowly down the main street. It was festooned with white ribbons, but the sign on the back didn't read, "Just Married," it read: "Just Divorced—still Best Friends!"

Treat your friends as you do your pictures, and place them in their best light.
JENNIE JEROME CHURCHILL

Friendship is love without his wings.
LORD BYRON

A successful marriage requires falling in love many times, always with the same person.
MIGNON McLAUGHLIN

Marrying to increase love is like gaming to become rich;
you only lose what little stock you had before.
WILLIAM WYCHERLEY

THEMES
■ MARRIAGE ■ FRIENDSHIP
■ DIVORCE ■ PEER PRESSURE

Not Such A Good Idea...

The assignment was to write an essay on some aspect of the city's history. The class had been given ample time to do the research required and the completed paper was now due.

In desperation, one incurable procrastinator named Judy was frantically trying to accomplish in one evening at the local library what she should have been working on for weeks. As she frowned at the computer screen's long list of articles, she realised there was no way she could hope to have an essay ready for the next day's class. What to do? Suddenly an idea came to her...

The following day, the teacher announced that she would read the best essays aloud. She read one, praised the effort, and before going on to the next one said: "Judy's paper, which I am about to read, is an excellent example of what I had in mind." The class looked in amazement at Judy. She did not exactly have a reputation as a good student, to say the least. Their amazement grew as they listened to the well researched and well written essay.

Half way through the reading, an even more amazing fact became apparent: As she continued on with the essay, the teacher was not looking at the paper any more! She obviously knew it by heart!

Poor Judy's face was growing redder by the minute... At last, the teacher stopped. "Judy," she said gently. "It's always wrong to copy someone else's work and pass it off as your own. But you made a further mistake when you failed to notice that your teacher wrote the piece you copied!"

It is an undoubted truth, that the less one has to do, the less time one has to do it in... One procrastinates, one can do it when one will, and therefore one seldom does it at all.
PHILIP STANHOPE, EARL OF CHESTERFIELD

He is only honest who is not discovered.
SUSANNAH CENTLIVRE

Honesty is the best policy.
ENGLISH PROVERB

THEMES
■ **CHEATING** ■ **HONESTY**
■ **PROCRASTINATION**

Crossing the Desert

If Jesus Christ had been a Dervish teacher instead of a Rabbi, he might not have told us about the grain of wheat that has to die in order to live. He might have told us this ancient tale instead:

A lovely stream flowed freely down a mountain and through a grassy plain until she reached the edge of a desert. There she soon found her waters turning muddy and drying up.

Despite this distressing fact, she always wanted to cross the desert.

"You can cross the desert if you want to," a voice said. "The wind does it all the time."

"But I am not the wind," objected the stream indignantly, and she thought the suggestion very silly.

"The wind can carry you," went on the voice. "Of course you will have to let it absorb you first."

The stream thought about that idea and found it repugnant. What if she lost her unique personality forever? How could she be sure she would be a stream again once she was on the other side?

"You will just have to trust my experience," replied the wind, reading her thoughts. "There's no other way."

"Ah, but I can choose to forget all about crossing the desert and just keep on as I am," said the stream defiantly.

"No, you can't," replied the voice with calm logic. "You will eventually turn into an ugly swamp. But if you let the wind carry you across the desert, you will be a beautiful stream again on the other side."

"The very same stream?" insisted the doubter.

The voice was relentless. "The essence of what you are as a stream—anyway, you can't stay the same even if you remain here. I've already told you, you'll end up a swamp!"

So the stream let herself be taken up as vapor and carried by the wind. High over the desert she sailed and when they reached the mountain on the other side, the wind let her fall gently as rain. Soon she was a beautiful, clear stream again, bubbling merrily along.

I silently laugh at my own cenotaph
And out of the caverns of rain,
Like a child from the womb, like a ghost
from the tomb,
I arise and unbuild it again.
PERCY BYSSHE SHELLEY

Doubt indulged soon becomes doubt realised.
FRANCES RIDLEY HAVERGAL

There is a divine plan of good at work in my life.
I will let go and let it unfold.
RUTH P. FREEDMAN

You must do the thing you think you cannot do.
ELEANOR ROOSEVELT

Faith begins as an experiment and
ends as an experience.
DEAN W. R. INGE

THEMES
■ TRUST ■ DEATH ■ LIFE
■ AFTERLIFE ■ DOUBT ■ FAITH
■ IDENTITY ■ OPENNESS

The Right Scent

There was once a garbage collector who was working so hard he fell in a heap from over-exertion. People gathered around and a woman took a bottle of perfume from her bag to try to revive him. But the sweet aroma failed to arouse him in the slightest.

Another tried a small bag of potpourri, but had no more success than her predecessor.

Then a fellow "garbo" had an idea. Opening one of the bags of garbage on the truck, he thrust a fistful of its contents under the fallen man's nose. Within seconds the man began to stir.

*Do not do unto others as you would they should do unto you.
Their tastes may not be the same.*
GEORGE BERNARD SHAW

Differences challenge assumptions.
ANNE WILSON SCHAEF

*The idea of God is different in every person. The joy
of my recovery was to find God within ME.*
ANGELA L. WOZNIAK

THEMES
■ TASTES ■ FAMILIARITY
■ DIFFERENCE

On Miami Beach

In one of Miami Beach's most luxurious resorts, amid spectacular entertainment, stunning views, the choicest of foods, beautiful pools and spas, beautiful people, wonderful opportunities to enjoy the best life has to offer, a guest noticed an elderly widower. He was huddled in a corner out of the sun, completely alone, playing Solitaire and sipping a glass of water.

His body couldn't take the exercise, his stomach couldn't take the food, his eyes couldn't take the sun, and his desires were for comfort and quiet, not nightclubs and fun.

By the time the old man could afford Miami Beach, Miami Beach had nothing to offer him.

*A man is never as unhappy as he thinks nor as
happy as he had hoped.*
FRANCIS, DUKE OF ROCHEFOUCAULD

*The sun has set in your life; it is getting cold.
The hundreds of people around you cannot console
you for the loss of the one.*
MARIE AUGUSTA TRAPP

*You don't seem to realize that a poor person who is unhappy
is in a better position than a rich person who is unhappy.
Because the poor person has hope.
He thinks money would help.*
JEAN KERR

THEMES
■ ELDERLY ■ TASTES ■ COMFORT
■ MONEY ■ PLEASURE ■ HAPPINESS

The "T" on the End

There is a story told about actor Jean Harlow which well illustrates the risks we run when trying to sound as if we're on familiar terms with famous people we hardly know.

In the days when her self-esteem apparently needed some shoring up, the screen star wanted to appear to be on a first-name basis with a well-known member of the nobility, Countess Margot Asquith.

The problem was that Jean kept pronouncing "Margot" incorrectly. Not realising that the last letter of the name is silent, each time she addressed the countess her "t" was very audible.

Finally, the countess lost her patience. "My dear," she said (doubtless in a tone that commanded attention), "the 't' is silent. As in 'Harlow.'"

*Live simply, not only within yourself but also in
your everyday dealings. Don't make ripples all
around you, don't try so hard to be interesting, keep
your distance, be honest, fight the desire to be
thought fascinating by the outside world.*
ETTY HILLESUM

*One must be leery of words because
they turn into cages.*
VIOLA SPOLIN

*You can't be truly rude until you understand
good manners.*
RITA MAE BROWN

*Do not compare yourself with others, for you
are a unique and wonderful creation. Make your own
beautiful footprints in the snow.*

BARBARA KIMBALL

THEMES
■ APPEARANCES ■ AMBITION
■ SIMPLICITY ■ GOOD MANNERS
■ RUDENESS

The Red-Capped Statuettes

Visitors to Tokyo's Zojogi Temple are greeted with the strange sight of rows and rows of little stone figures, all alike in their red knitted caps, tiny bibs and pinwheels at their sides. The figures stand for aborted babies. The names of their mothers are inscribed on cups placed in front of each tiny statue.

The cost of a statue, together with maintenance for one year, is 7,000 yen. For another 6,300 yen the memorial ceremony called "mizuko kuyo" will be celebrated for the unborn child. The ceremony is intended to bring peace to the child and to ask the goddess (represented by a statue at the end of each row of child-statues) to take the baby across the River Sai to its ancestors. Happy there, it will not return to upset the parents or cause sorrow.

Parents also buy wooden plaques and inscribe them with messages to the unborn. The plaques can be read by visitors who will find them hanging in a covered walkway nearby. One of the most poignant reads:

"You are our baby, I will never forget you. From the bottom of my heart, I ask forgiveness forever and ever."

There are some 20,000 little stone statues in Zojogi Temple.

It is by forgiving that one is forgiven.
MOTHER TERESA

We can never go back again, that much is certain.
DAPHNE DuMAURIER

There is a remedy for everything except death.
LATIN PROVERB

THEMES
■ **ABORTION** ■ **REMORSE**
■ **FORGIVENESS** ■ **REPARATION**

Wearing the Star

During the time of the Nazi occupation of France, Jews were forced to wear a very visible Star of David so that they would be clearly set apart from their fellow citizens.

The famous philosopher Henri Bergson, though a Jew, was not required to wear the Star—indeed the authorities did not want him to wear it because of his international repute and the embarrassment such public evidence of Nazi anti-Semitism could cause the regime.

Bergson had long leaned toward Catholicism. His two close associates, the well-known Jacques and Raissa Maritain, had both become Catholics and were distinguishing themselves for brilliant treatises in neo-Scholasticism—an updated philosophy of St Thomas Aquinas.

But to the dismay of the Nazis, Henri Bergson, old and feeble, yet venerable in his quiet dignity, insisted on appearing with his fellow Jews in a long queue on the streets, his Star of David plainly visible to all.

As he explained to friends, whatever his religious views might be, the times called for solidarity with his persecuted brethren. Powerless to do more, he would at least give witness and silently protest the injustice being done. The integrity he had taught as a philosopher was translated into his very life.

We hold these truths to be self-evident, that all men are created equal, that they are endowed by their Creator with certain unalienable rights, that among these are life, liberty and the pursuit of happiness.
**THOMAS JEFFERSON,
AMERICAN DECLARATION OF INDEPENDENCE**

To keep your character intact you cannot stoop to filthy acts. It makes it easier to stoop the next time.
KATHARINE HEPBURN

No trumpets sound when the important decisions of our life are made. Destiny is made known silently.
AGNES DeMILLE

**THEMES
▪ INTEGRITY ▪ SOLIDARITY
▪ PERSECUTION ▪ RELIGION
▪ EQUALITY ▪ TRUTH**

Why Him?

There was a pool in Jerusalem which was supposed to have healing powers. A lot of disabled and sick people gathered around there hoping to be cured.

Jesus came along one day, walked around among all those suffering people, and stopped by just one man. He spoke with that man briefly and then healed him.

As far as the Gospel story goes, he was the only one Jesus favored that day at the pool. Was it because that man had waited forty years for a miraculous cure? Were all the other sufferers passed by because they had only waited ten or twenty or thirty—or thirty-nine-and-a-half years?! Was forty the magic number required for a cure?

A contemplative once answered the question this way:

"Forty years or one day of waiting—it's immaterial. Jesus would have cured anybody else there *who was ready*. He cured the only person who was completely open to his healing power."

Is there ever any particular spot where one can put one's finger and say, 'It all began that day, at such a time and place, with such an incident'?
AGATHA CHRISTIE

You can have anything you want if you want it desperately enough. You must want it with an inner exuberance that erupts through the skin and joins the energy that created the world.
SHEILAH GRAHAM

How rash to assert that man shapes his own destiny! All he can do is determine his inner responses.
ETTY HILLESUM

If heaven drops a date, open your mouth!
CHINESE PROVERB

THEMES
▪ HEALING ▪ READINESS ▪ ATTITUDE
▪ CHOICE ▪ OPPORTUNITY

Two Ways Up

A very poor house, little more than a shack, huddled close to the huge cement foundations of a giant luxury block. In that cottage lived an immigrant family. The two girls of the family were bright and ambitious, and all their aspirations had crystallised around the penthouse at the top of the gleaming apartment building. "Someday . . . someday," they would say, "we will be rich enough to buy that penthouse."

"And bring the whole family up there to live!" That was the dream of Jean, the oldest.

"Imagine the power and prestige we'd have!" her sister Ann would murmur.

The difference between the two girls only became evident when they reached their teens and young adulthood. Whereas Jean studied hard and eventually became a famous surgeon, Ann always looked for ways of making a fast buck without much thought of right or wrong.

When they reached their forties, both were rich and both were able to afford penthouses like the one they had admired as children. But while Jean was respected and loved by family, friends and colleagues, Ann had caused so much suffering to so many as she clawed her way to the top that there was now no one to share her wealth and power.

An old man who had lived in the neighborhood for thirty years was asked about the spectacular rise of the two well-known sisters who had started life in a shack.

"Well," he said after a moment, "there are many ways of reaching the pinnacle those girls were aiming for. A young eagle practices flying until he can soar to those heights. A rat gets there by scurrying up the drainpipes." And he would say no more.

*A characteristic thing about the aspiring immigrant is
the fact that he is not content to progress alone.
Solitary success is imperfect success in his eyes.
He must take his family with him as he rises.*
MARY ANTIN

*She's the kind of woman who climbed the ladder of
success—wrong by wrong.*
MAE WEST

It's them that take advantage that get advantage in this world.
GEORGE ELIOT

*They who are of the opinion that money will do
everything may very well be suspected of doing
everything for money.*
GEORGE SAVILLE

Poverty of goods is easily cured; poverty of soul, impossible.
MICHELE DE MONTAIGNE

THEMES
■ AMBITION ■ SUCCESS ■ MONEY
■ WEALTH ■ POWER

Ingenuity

....

The nuns of a certain convent earned their living making exquisite vestments for liturgical celebrations. Each creation was a masterpiece, unique and original in its embroidered designs. Of particular note were the vibrant colors of the embroidery—under the lights in church the reds, golds, silvers, greens and blues seemed to glow and sparkle with a life of their own.

"What magical threads those nuns must use!" thought one admiring churchgoer. "Surely the metallic threads are the secret. They must send away for the very best and pay a fortune for them."

Wondering how cloistered nuns could afford such materials, the curious woman decided to investigate. To her utter astonishment, she learned that the vestment-makers used nothing but the spool-ends discarded by the nearby city's garment manufacturers. "Do you mean to say," she exclaimed to the nun who told her, "that instead of ordering special threads for your needs, you people are creating your designs around the hundreds of donated spool-ends?"

"That's absolutely right," replied the sister. "Just goes to prove the old saying: 'One person's cast-offs become another person's treasure.'"

There are painters who transform the sun into a yellow spot, but there are others who, thanks to their art and intelligence, transform a yellow spot into the sun.
PABLO PICASSO

Man [or woman!] must make opportunity, as oft as find it.
FRANCIS BACON

I believe that true identity is found... in creative activity springing from within... Woman can best re-find herself by losing herself in some kind of creative activity of her own.

ANNE MORROW LINDBERGH

Genius is an infinite capacity for taking life by the scruff of the neck.

CHRISTOPHER QUILL

THEMES
▪ CREATIVITY ▪ COMPETENCE ▪ SKILL
▪ EXPERTISE ▪ OPPORTUNITY

A Fable of Partnership

At a dinner party a wealthy financier confided to his host that he would like to start a business but did not have any original ideas or products in mind. That same evening in another part of the room, another guest said in the course of chatting, "I've invented a wonderful new toaster but I have no capital to set up a manufacturing business." The host overheard the remark.

Being the type who likes to make things happen, she introduced the two men to each other. Before they had time to wonder why she had brought them together, she said, "May I share an interesting fable with you?" Without waiting for an answer, she told this story:

"A lame man had received an invitation to a great banquet. As he read the golden scroll, his face grew sad. 'How can I go to the Sultan's dinner?' he moaned. 'I am so shrivelled and crippled.'

"Near him in the inn's dining room, another man, a big strong fellow, was handed an identical scroll. But he was blind, so someone had to read his invitation to him. 'Poor me!' he moaned. 'How can I get to the palace if I cannot see the way?'

"The jolly innkeeper heard the moaning of both men. 'Look, you two,' he called. 'If the little fellow climbs on the blind man's back, you'll have a pair of good eyes and legs between the two of you! So off you go now!' "

As the host moved away, she concluded her story. "It's so nice," she said, "when vision and means get together."

A bird never flew on one wing.
SCOTTISH PROVERB

The greatest gift we can give one another is rapt attention to one another's existence.
SUE ATCHLEY EBAUGH

The unity of man is based upon his infinite diversity.
VANCE PALMER

We plough along, as the fly said to the ox.
HENRY WADSWORTH LONGFELLOW

THEMES
■ COOPERATION ■ CREATIVITY
■ OPPORTUNITY ■ HARMONY
■ HANDICAPS

Buried Treasure

The famous Franciscan thirteenth-century scholar, Roger Bacon, published the following story, but its origins go back over a thousand years. It has enjoyed incredible popularity as an illustration of the fact that people may develop certain abilities while all their efforts are intent on quite different goals.

"The Tale of the Greedy Sons" carries with it, in most versions, the promise that those who pass it on will gain unimagined benefits (hence its widespread popularity!).

The farmer in the story was a very wealthy, hard-working man, but his sons were all lazy and greedy. Before he died, he told them that they would find his treasures buried in the fields. Naturally, as soon as he was gone they rushed to the fields and dug furiously.

All their efforts to find the treasure, however, proved fruitless. "Well," said one, "since the fields are all plowed, we might as well plant a crop." This they did and it produced a rich and profitable harvest. They lived that year on the sale of their crop but then decided to try for the treasure again. The same thing happened: no gold, but another profitable crop.

This went on for several years. The once lazy sons were now used to working hard and living on the fruits of their labor. They had become efficient, happy men of the land, almost without being aware of it.

"This is what Father knew would happen!" one of them suddenly realised. "This is the inheritance he left us!"

A human being must have occupation if he or she is not to become a nuisance to the world.

DOROTHY L. SAYERS

*All of the fantasies in your life will never match
those I once tried to attain. Now older, it's more
important reaching the more realistic goals,
and having them come true.*
DEIDRA SARAULT

I have seen the future, and it works.
LINCOLN STEFFENS

The end crowns the work.
LATIN SAYING

THEMES
■ SURPRISE ■ GREED ■ LABOR
■ CHANGE ■ MOTIVATION

Which Plague?

In Lahore, Pakistan, there is a shrine to Sheikh Qalandar Shah, whose famous book of teachings can be translated into English as "The Recluse's Secrets." My favorite story from this collection is one about misinformation.

One day, in a certain town, a man crossed from one street into another. Children playing on the second street noticed tears streaming down his cheeks.

"Someone must have died on his street," one child said. Before you knew it, the word had spread that a terrible tragedy had occurred.

No one wanted to make impertinent enquiries in a time of sorrow, so it was difficult for adults on both streets to get to the facts. Some people then concluded that an infectious disease must be the reason for the cover-up. Each street's inhabitants came to think that the plague must be raging on the other street.

Like a flash, the word went around that survival depended on getting out of the town as fast as possible. Naturally, neighbors stuck together and made sure not to mix with groups from the other street.

Imagine if all those people had known that the man's tears on that day had actually come from peeling onions!

If you visit the region today, you will find a ghost town with two prosperous villages nearby. Each village has a different story as to the founding of their community but both are certain it has something to do with getting away from a devastating plague in the nick of time.

Fame or report commonly receives an addition when it goes from hand to hand.
SCOTTISH PROVERB

Rumor is untraceable, incalculable, and infectious.
MARGOT ASQUITH

Sane people did what their neighbors did, so that if any lunatics were at large, one might know and avoid them.
NORA EPHRON

THEMES
▪ RUMOR ▪ EXAGGERATION
▪ MISINFORMATION

The Hated Staff

You may have read the Bible story about the poor widow who fed a prophet in a time of famine and was rewarded for her charity with a miraculous jug that never went dry. Perhaps the widow of my tale was remembering the biblical narrative when she took in a destitute holy man. At any rate, sure enough, on his departure the holy man gave the widow and her son a miraculous staff which would always provide them with their needs.

Imagine their joy when first they tried it out! Food, clothing, shelter—whenever the staff was waved in time of need, the money required would appear!

One day, the young man said: "This is fine, but what about our future, Mother? We need to have something extra put away. Let us ask for a bit more than what we really need." The woman wanted to protest that the genie in the staff would probably not be fooled, but she said nothing.

The boy made his attempt at deception, but at once the staff turned into a dry old stick with no powers at all. Just then the holy man returned. To the boy he said, "Your dishonesty has sprung from your fear of not having enough. However, you are still young and I can teach you wisdom.

"But you," he said to the woman, "you knew better, yet said nothing because you were afraid to lose your son's affection. Your fear is the fear of not being needed." Angrily the woman snapped, "Right you are! I hated that old staff because he counted on it more than on me!"

The holy man then invited the young man to come away with him so that both mother and son could learn to be truly free.

No passion so effectually robs the mind of all its
powers of acting and reasoning as fear.
EDMUND BURKE

*You are going to let the fear of poverty govern
your life and your reward will be that you will eat, but
you will not live.*
GEORGE BERNARD SHAW

*A codependent person is one who has let another person's
behavior affect him or her, and who is obsessed with
controlling that person's behavior.*
MELODIE BEATTIE

*Freedom has a thousand charms to show
That slaves, howe'er contented, never know.*
WILLIAM COWPER

THEMES
■ FEAR ■ DECEPTION ■ HONESTY
■ CODEPENDENCY ■ SECURITY ■ FREEDOM

Important Secrets

At an international seminar held in Australia, Aboriginal speaker
Eddie Kneebone explained the sense of importance his people were
able to impart to their children when they still lived "in the old way"
on their land. A feeling of insignificance or despair leading to
suicide—all too common today among young adults—was unlikely
then because of a unique custom:

At a certain predetermined time, a young person would be
solemnly entrusted with a secret piece of knowledge—information
that could prove vital to the tribe's survival. It might be the location
of a hidden waterhole in one area of their territory. It might be the
medicinal powers of a certain plant. No one else in the tribe would be

given that piece of important knowledge and when the time came, this young person would be expected to contribute it for the welfare of all.

"Imagine," concluded Eddie, "what a sense of importance and belonging this custom gave our young people. Each of them had a unique place, each had an undeniably important role to play.

"Self-esteem and a sense of personal worth were the great benefits of this Aboriginal custom—long before any psychologist told us about these elements of healthy growth!"

He who despises himself esteems himself as a self-despiser.
SUSAN SONTAG

You can be pleased with nothing when you are not pleased with yourself.
LADY MARY WORTLEY MONTAGUE

The worth of a State, in the long run, is the worth of the individuals composing it.
JOHN STUART MILL

THEMES
■ SELF-ESTEEM ■ SUICIDE
■ YOUTH ■ ABORIGINAL
■ INDIGENOUS ■ CUSTOM

When Sunnie Got Angry

A woman was having lunch in London's Dorchester Hotel in 1942. Her tablemates were some girlfriends and a group of young soldiers who had been badly burned on the battlefield. The woman had the unusual nickname of Sunnie and had been driving ambulances in the Blitz. Wanting to do more, she had convinced the famous Hotel to begin offering free lunches for burns victims.

At this particular lunch, she was taken by surprise when the head waiter came to tell her that other diners had registered a complaint: their meal, they said, was being ruined by the presence of the veterans with their repulsive burns...

Sunnie got up and, having learned from the waiter which guests had complained, approached their table. To her polite enquiry, "Are you English?" the diners replied that they certainly were.

Then in tones that belied the nature from which her nickname had come, Sunnie furiously demanded to know how they could complain about boys who had been burned fighting to save their very lives.

"Because they have burned faces, you can't enjoy your dinner?" she cried. "Well, too damned bad!" And with that, she picked up a glass of water and threw it in their faces.

This same woman won the world's admiration some fifty years later when her husband, Jackie Mann, was taken hostage in Beirut. Though alone, without friends, income, water or electricity, she refused to leave Lebanon and doggedly fought to keep her husband's tragic situation before the public eye. When the elderly couple were finally reunited after his release, an official commented on Sunnie's courage. Her response echoed her wet defence of the young burns victims: "I survive because I'm so damn stubborn!"

You were there when I needed you. You stood above
all of the others with your strength and
you guided me.
DEIDRA SARAULT

A great many people think they are thinking when
they are only rearranging their prejudice.
ATTRIBUTED TO WILLIAM JAMES

You gain strength, courage and confidence by
every experience by which you really stop to look
fear in the face.
ELEANOR ROOSEVELT

When the going gets tough, the tough get going.
JOSEPH P. KENNEDY

THEMES
■ COURAGE ■ COMPASSION
■ KINDNESS ■ PREJUDICE

Double Take

In a certain camp, refugees lined up each day at a prescribed hour to receive food and other necessities. After a while, people noticed that one woman always got into line a second time and received another portion.

At first, no one said anything. People who have suffered a lot usually assume that only great hardship can cause someone to overstep the mark. "She must be hungrier than all of us," they said to one another. "After a week or so, she will not need to do this."

But the weeks went by and the woman continued the pattern—except that her second appearance came at different times and sometimes she tied a different scarf around her neck so that she wasn't too obvious. "Must still be desperate," people said.

Finally they lost patience. "Greedy woman!" they confronted her one day. "What do you think you are doing? You don't fool us!" At that the woman broke down and sobbed out her story. "The second lot is not for me. My son hides under our blanket because he is so burned and disfigured. He will starve if I don't go back to get a portion for him!"

Saddened, the others moved aside to let her pass. "We will not tell on you," they whispered in sympathy. "Continue to stand in the line for him." The woman moved off, bowed under her pain. She had not gone far when she realised that a few of the group had started to follow her. Soon others joined them.

"They do not believe me," she thought sadly, more crushed than ever. But the voice of a young man at the head of the group surprised her. "Wait!" he called. "We can give more than that food portion. We will come to be friends with your son and keep him company and help him forget his burns."

And that newfound acceptance was more healing than anything the poor woman could get in the food line.

73

Everything that we really accept undergoes a change.
So suffering must become love. That is the mystery.
KATHERINE MANSFIELD

Love and the hope of it are not things one can learn;
they are a part of life's heritage.
MARIA MONTESSORI

Love will find a way.
ENGLISH PROVERB

Such ever was love's way; to rise, it stoops.
ROBERT BROWNING

THEMES
■ ACCEPTANCE ■ LOVE
■ COMPASSION ■ FRIENDSHIP
■ KINDNESS ■ EMPATHY

The Sobbing Pond

Once upon a time, in a world faraway—yes, this is a fairy tale—there was a land of lovely lakes and rivers. In summer people swam and fished and boated and snorkled and whitewater-rafted. In winter they cut out holes in the ice to fish and of course they skated and played ice hockey. Visitors to the country all remarked on the fresh sparkling water that seemed to be everywhere, the wonderful fish in the markets and the healthy children, so at home in the water and on the ice. Life was fairly simple, with most people making their living by farming or fishing.

One day a big businessman came in a stretch limo and began saying how sorry he felt for the people of this country because they weren't urbanized or industrialized. He started to make some changes.

To make a long story short—yes, you guessed it!—after only a few years, there were factories and cities everywhere. Many of the ponds were filled in to allow for more buildings.

Although people said, "We'll make sure to preserve most of the ponds and we won't touch the lakes," that's not what happened, of course. Still more industrial sites were called for, so they filled in all the ponds and then they started on the lakes... Soon the lovely rivers and streams were polluted by the factory waste and the fish could no longer be eaten. The land began to dry up and crack and the topsoil blew away.

At last there was only one little pond left. Small children came from all over the land to look at it because they had never known the lakes and rivers of sparkling water. But the old folks stood by in great sadness. They looked as withered up as the dry lakes and river beds of their once lovely land.

After the last drops of water disappeared from the last pond, a strange thing happened. One hundred very elderly men and women ringed the pond in silence, their eyes and mouths drooped in great sorrow. Soon another hundred joined them in the circle. No one spoke but, very softly, the first old man who had come to the site began to cry. As his sobs grew louder, others joined in and their wailing could be heard for miles. In a day or so more people came to encircle the dry pond. And they too sobbed...

All around the pond bed the sobs rose and the tears fell—hundreds, then thousands, then millions of tears poured down the furrowed cheeks and onto the parched ground until—yes, you guessed it!—a pure crystal pond began to appear again!

The very old man who had first begun to sob at the pond died of a broken heart before he ever saw the new pond take shape. No one knew his name, but as they began to clean up their rivers and reclaim their lakes, the people spoke in hushed tones about the wonderful thing he had done. Eventually they decided to pull down the statue of the big businessman and erect a monument to the old man.

Now as I said, this is just a fairy tale, but I thought you'd like to hear what they wrote beneath the statue. The inscription read: "To our Sobbing Savior: thank you for dying crying." And of course they built a church on the spot because no one doubted that God was there.

Tears are like rain. They loosen up our soil so we can grow in different directions.
VIRGINIA CASEY

Something has gone unspeakably wrong... we human beings have made a terminal mess of this earth.
LISA WEIL

How can the spirit of the earth like the white man?... Everywhere the white man has touched it, it is sore.
PRETTY SHIELD

THEMES
▪ ECOLOGY ▪ WATER ▪ CONSERVATION
▪ GRIEF ▪ SALVATION ▪ RESOURCES
▪ ENVIRONMENT ▪ PROGRESS

All That Jazz!

John Hammond, the famous American record producer, had a unique genius for discovering talent. He began his career in jazz and was responsible for the meteoric rise to fame of such greats as Count Basie, Billie Holliday and Benny Goodman. Unlike many of us, Hammond was never locked into the disastrous mindset that condemns anything new, so in later years he recognised and promoted very different types of musicians, such as Pete Seeger, Bob Dylan and Bruce Springsteen.

What may not be so well known was his dedication to racial justice and integration at all costs. Through his efforts, Benny Goodman's band was composed of both blacks and whites. He gave his support to the first integrated nightclub, called the Cafe Society, and succeeded in getting Billie Holliday to sing there. During the second World War, while white soldiers like himself were provided with the best of entertainers, Hammond's concern reached out to the Negro regiments and he harassed enough officials to obtain top class acts, like Count Basie, for their entertainment.

But it was the first Newport Jazz Festival that became a legend and a memorial to what one person can do for justice within his or her own working milieu. John Hammond wanted to ensure its success by bringing his top talent, but one thing he stipulated as an absolute condition was that the whole festival, all accommodations in the city and all eating places as well, would have to be open to both blacks and whites. Such integration caused gasps of concern in those pre-civil-rights days: would this policy ruin the whole project? John was adamant: either there would be full racial integration or none of his singing stars would be there!

He won the day for racial equality—and the Newport Jazz Festival was a resounding success!

There's no question in my mind but that rights are never won unless people are willing to fight for them.

ELEANOR SMEAD

Saints are non-conformists.

ELEANOR RICE TAYLOR

Delay of justice is injustice.

WALTER SAVAGE LANDOR

THEMES
■ EQUALITY ■ RACISM ■ CIVIL RIGHTS
■ COURAGE ■ JUSTICE ■ GREATNESS

The Nightingale Tale

The widow had heard the strange legend of the nightingales and decided to set off to see for herself whether the tale had any truth to it. "A submerged city!" scoffed her neighbors. "Nightingales singing from submerged bell towers! What nonsense!" But the sad, sombre widow replied: "I know that I shall probably be disillusioned. I shall probably hear nothing at all. But I cannot help but hope. The legend goes that one who waits by the site of the submerged city with the proper dispositions will certainly hear the song of the nightingales."

The neighbors shook their heads. "Her problem is that she will not let us help her or comfort her or cheer her," they said to one another. "She insists on trying to go it alone. Can't seem to accept help. Stubborn old fool!"

When the widow arrived at the site of the submerged city, she set up camp on the shore, with tent and provisions. A day went by, then a week, then a month. Several people from a nearby village came to offer friendly assistance, but the widow did not want help. "I can manage alone," she said.

The second month went by. A stray dog came sniffing around her tent, wanting to belong to someone. "Be off!" she cried. "I cannot be of help to you. I'm no good for myself or anyone else." Then she added softly to herself, "But maybe everything will change... when I hear the nightingales sing."

The weather turned colder. Winter was coming. The widow had now been camped by the sea for four months. She still had some money left and each week she would go into the nearby village to buy food and firewood, but she exchanged no greetings with anyone and looked neither left nor right on her way. Each time she arrived back at the camp, she would dare to think, "Now, maybe..." But no sound broke the silence.

One day the widow was gathering some kindling wood to start her fire when she tripped and twisted her ankle. "What bad luck," she sighed. "Now what will I do?" She had lain there only a few minutes when the stray dog ambled into view. But this time he looked happier. Forgetting herself, the widow exclaimed, "Good for you, little pup!" And she fed him meat from a sandwich she had in her knapsack.

The dog bounded off and, as he went, suddenly the widow thought she heard wonderful music from afar. She lay perfectly still so as to hear better, but all was silent. "Silly old woman," she scolded herself. "Forget your nightingale fantasy and figure out how to get yourself out of this mess."

Just then a group of villagers came into view, led by the pup. "You are hurt," said one of the elders. "Please let us help you. You need friends."

The widow's stubborn pride melted. "Yes," she said, "I need help. I need friends. Too long have I tried to go it alone. I preferred to look for help from a fantasy of nightingales rather than from ordinary people like myself. I do need you. Thank you for coming."

And right then not only the widow but the whole town heard an incredible outpouring of the sweetest music imaginable! The nightingales were sending cascades of marvelous notes ringing through the air, carried by the wind into every town and home and heart, to banish sorrow and pain.

Today if you go into that region you will surely hear the legend told and retold but now it is called "The story of the widow's nightingales."

The change of one simple behavior can affect other behaviors and thus change many things.
JEAN BAER

Some of us let great dreams die, but others nourish and protect them through bad days till they bring them to the sunshine and light which comes always to those who sincerely hope that their dreams will come true.
WOODROW WILSON

The miserable have no other medicine,
But only hope.
WILLIAM SHAKESPEARE

THEMES
▪ ACCEPTANCE ▪ GRIEF ▪ HELP
▪ PRIDE ▪ FRIENDSHIP ▪ HOPE

Oh, To Be Sizable

··

There is an old American Negro tale about a dwarf called Knee-high Man who longed to be tall—"tall and sizable" was how he put it. So he decided to enquire of his animal friends how he might grow.

Horse was most willing to help but naturally his advice reflected his own experience. "Eat lots of corn, do a lot of running and you'll surely grow tall."

It sounded like a lot of hard work, but the little man was very anxious to improve his stature, so he both ate and ran until he nearly dropped. Tired he became, sick in the tummy, too, but grow he did not.

His next approach was to Bull, who also was most obliging. "Eat a lot of grass," said Bull, "and roar like I do over and over again. You will surely grow."

"Much obliged," said the little man and proceeded to do what Bull had said. Tired he became, sick in the tummy, too, but grow he did not.

He thought, then, of wise old Owl. "How can I become sizable?" he asked Owl. Owl did not reply for a moment. He seemed to be deep in thought. At last he hooted solemnly and asked a question of his own: "Why do you want to grow tall?"

Knee-high Man was surprised at the question. But in a flash he had the answer. "So I won't be beaten when I gets in a fight!"

"Have you ever been in a fight?" enquired wise old Owl.

"No-o-o," murmured Knee-high Man, a bit embarrassed. But then he added, "Yet, that is."

"Well, you ain't got no cause yet to want to be sizable then, far as I can see," concluded the old bird and started to close his eyes.

"Wait, wait!" cried the little man. "I need to be sizable so I can see far into the distance."

"Ain't you ever climbed a tree to get a long-distance look?" asked Owl.

"Well, y-e-e-s," murmured Knee-high Man, more embarrassed than before. Again the old bird's eyes began to shut, but just before they closed altogether, he said firmly, "Ain't nothing wrong with your body size, my friend. It's your brain that needs growing!"

I think knowing what you can not do is more important than knowing what you can do. In fact, that's good taste.

LUCILLE BALL

A word to the wise is enough.

LATIN PROVERB

There is no better looking-glass than an old friend.

17TH CENTURY ENGLISH PROVERB

Life is made up of desires that seem big and vital one minute and absurd the next. I guess we get what's best for us in the end.

ALICE CALDWELL RICE

THEMES

■ GROWTH ■ WISDOM ■ DISCONTENT
■ ACCEPTANCE ■ FRIENDSHIP ■ DESIRE

On The Corner

Older Brother and Younger Brother left home together after receiving their share of their parents' estate. Each had been given the same amount, but before long, Older Brother had managed to cheat his brother out of his share. Younger Brother ended up homeless and hungry in the poorest part of town, while his brother started gambling and living it up.

Despite his misfortune, Younger Brother set his mind on positive thinking, refusing to dwell on the injustice done him. This attitude left him free to pay close attention to everything that went on around him. Before long he had a job as a storeman and packer, and he had made a few friends. When job opportunities came up in his company, he recommended these friends.

Word got around and Younger Brother gradually became known in his neighborhood as a very hardworking and kind young man. Ray the fruitstand man offered him a partnership in his new and bigger stand. Dolly the hairdresser on the corner lent him the money to put a down payment on a unit. Two salesmen, whom he had helped get work, organized his campaign when he decided to run for office.

Meanwhile across town, Older Brother had fallen on hard times. He looked up Younger Brother, having heard that he was now in local government. In fact, hard as he found it to believe, it seemed that Younger Brother had done quite well for himself! He made up his mind to find out his secret—how had he turned his life around?

"Well, it's this neighborhood," answered Younger Brother. "I got all my opportunities right at this intersection."

So Older Brother hung around the area night and day, day and night. But he never saw anyone who seemed important or wealthy or powerful ("just ordinary hairdressers and fruitstand vendors and the like") and he grew more puzzled and angry each day. At last he moved off in disgust, telling himself that Younger Brother had pulled a smart one on him ("just like I'd have done to him," he said to himself).

*To my mind the best investment a young man starting out
in business could possibly make is to give all his time,
all his energies to work, just plain, hard work.*
CHARLES M. SCHWAB

*I must admit that I personally measure success in terms
of the contributions an individual makes to her or his
fellow human beings.*
MARGARET MEAD

*People are always blaming their circumstances for what
they are. I don't believe in circumstances. The people
who get on in this world are the people who get up and
look for the circumstances they want, and, if they
can't find them, make them.*
GEORGE BERNARD SHAW

*Genius is an infinite capacity for taking life
by the scruff of the neck.*
CHRISTOPHER QUILL

THEMES
■ OPPORTUNITY ■ LABOR ■ SUCCESS
■ KINDNESS ■ COMPETENCE ■ ATTITUDE

The Man in the Library

In the warm, comfortable reading room of the Morristown, New Jersey library, patrons were becoming increasingly annoyed by a certain strong smell. It came from a shabby, scruffy, bearded figure ensconced in one of the armchairs. There he was, day in and day out, with a book open in front of him, but everyone knew the library's chief attraction for this patron was its warmth and comfort.

Eventually annoyance reached a peak and the chief librarian felt impelled to call the police to rid his library of the unwashed tramp. But the man kept coming back. So the police kept throwing him out.

This homeless man's name was Richard Kreimer, and being excluded from the library seemed to be the final straw for Richard. He had been thrown out of boiler rooms and wrecked cars where he had taken shelter for the night; he had been made to "move on" out into the wet and cold more times than he could remember. But this time something broke within him and he decided to fight back. Did he want to become the shining knight of all the First World's forgotten poor? Who knows? The fact is that Richard Kreimer, with the help of a civil rights lawyer, took on City Hall—and won!

First he sued the library, claiming that he had a right to be there. He also sued the town council and six police officers who had forcibly ejected him. Having won that case, he next sued the State of New Jersey itself for refusing to let him vote on the grounds that he had no fixed address. He won again!

More confident now, Richard and his solicitor laid charges against five police officers whom he alleged had harassed and abused him, and against town officials whom he said had ignored his complaints.

By now the Morristown civil leaders were getting very nervous. Media people were pouring into town to do stories on Kreimer's successes—a modern David and Goliath tale that made great copy! To the fury of many townspeople the council decided to cut its losses, to negotiate an out-of-court settlement, offering the homeless man the staggering sum of $190,000. In return for the money, Kreimer was to drop charges and say no more to the media. The destitute man accepted the deal.

Another less obvious victory resulting from the whole affair was in favor of the homeless. Suddenly the tragedy of America's 33.6 million people living below the poverty level was dramatized as never before in the smelly, defiant figure of Richard Kreimer. As a result, the next time we walk past the inhabitants of doorways and park benches, we may do more than simply turn away.

Only those who dare, truly live.

RUTH P. FREEDMAN

We want people to feel with us more than to act for us.

GEORGE ELIOT

Poverty is not a crime.

ENGLISH PROVERB

I leave you, hoping that the lamp of liberty will burn in your bosoms, until there shall no longer be a doubt that all men are created free and equal.

ABRAHAM LINCOLN

THEMES
■ POVERTY ■ PREJUDICE
■ CIVIL RIGHTS ■ EQUALITY
■ JUSTICE ■ ACTION ■ NEGOTIATION

Who's Outsmarting Whom?

An Indonesian folktale tells of a tricky deer who often proved that the weak can outsmart the strong. In one instance, a lion catches him unawares and announces that he is about to have him for dinner. Crafty as always, the deer tells the lion that he would find a plump grown man a much better meal. Having aroused his curiosity and greed, he leads him to the roadside and together they wait for a man to come along. But just when the lion is about to pounce, the experienced hunter shoots him.

Free and safe, the deer bounds off. But it is not his day. Resting by the river, he is attacked by old Croc. With one of his legs already in the crocodile's jaws, the deer manages to con this enemy, too. "That's only a stick you've got hold of," he taunts. "See, here's my real leg," he yells, kicking his other leg past Croc's nose. The croc releases the first leg to lunge at the second, but quick as a flash the deer leaps away!

Proud of his feats, our friend comes upon a lowly snail crawling along at—you guessed it—a snail's pace. "Let's race," sneers Deer.

Now the little snail has waited a long time to get back at the deer, who regularly humiliates him with the "let's race" taunt. So he is ready for Deer this time. "Okay," he agrees, and off they start.

Deer tears along toward the finish line, but to his utter amazement, when he reaches it, Snail is already there ahead of him! "I can't believe this," he gasps. "Well, we'll see who gets back to Start first!" And he tears along at double his usual speed.

But when he arrives at the starting line, there is Snail, looking quite cool and triumphant. "Once more!" yells Deer, furious but unwilling to admit defeat. Yet once again he finds the snail has beat him to the line. Dumbfounded, he slinks off, hanging his head.

Much later in the day, two snails meet halfway between the start and finish lines. Grinning broadly, they congratulate each other. "We got him this time, we did!" You see, they look so much alike, poor Deer never realised he wasn't seeing the same competitor at the start and the finish.

The race is not to the swift, nor the battle to the strong.
THE BIBLE (ECCLES. 9:11)

It is hard to fight an enemy who has outposts in your head.
SALLY KEMPTON

*What makes us so bitter against people who outwit us is
that they think themselves cleverer than we are.*
FRANCOIS, DUC DE LA ROCHEFOUCAULD

THEMES
- VANITY - WEAKNESS
- STRENGTH - WISDOM
- CLEVERNESS - ENEMIES

A Revealing Stumble

A bishop was presiding over a graduation ceremony marked by proper pomp and circumstance. The line of graduates moved slowly up the steps to the stage where the diplomas were being handed out.

Suddenly a young woman stumbled and fell into the bishop's arms! There was stunned silence punctured by smothered gasps.

An accomplished performer at hundreds of such ceremonies, the unruffled bishop quipped: "This is the first time I've had a fallen woman in my arms!" The huge crowd broke into peals of appreciative laughter.

Equally quick on the uptake, the girl replied in clear tones, "And this is the first time I've been picked up by a bishop!"

The odd incident sometimes brings to the fore a hidden talent, but this stumble revealed *two* quick wits! What fall is waiting to reveal *my* special gifts? . . .

He that is down need fear no fall.
JOHN BUNYON

When we begin to take our failures non-seriously,
it means we are ceasing to be afraid of them.
It is of immense importance to learn to laugh
at ourselves.
KATHERINE MANSFIELD

Laugh and the world laughs with you.
HORACE

Humor distorts nothing and only false gods are
laughed off their earthly pedestals.
AGNES REPPLIER

THEMES
■ HUMOR ■ READINESS
■ ADAPTABILITY ■ DISCOVERY

Homemade

A Polish-Australian woman looks at her city of Canberra and its people in a way that is quite out of the ordinary. For her, the proud capital of Australia has a sad underside like any big city, and it is the citizens of this "other city" who most interest her.

Every Friday evening this woman in her sixties, whom we'll call Helen, moves from her own happy and secure world to Canberra's seedier areas. She sets up a few simple card tables in a prominent spot on a busy street and loads them up with all the food she has collected from friends and food stores, plus her homemade soup and other tasty items.

From Friday night to Sunday night she and other volunteers dispense food to the needy. Helen's food kitchen is undoubtedly the proverbial drop in the bucket, but its very simplicity allows for the personal quality that makes it unique.

Helen's attitude is the secret. She does not consider herself a professional welfare worker or charity volunteer. Nor does she consider the people she feeds as "the poor." Each is an individual to her, whom she looks forward to seeing. One incident typifies Helen's attitude:

A shabbily dressed man approached her tables and long before he was near, the smell of an unwashed body and reeking clothes preceded him. Totally unaware of all this, Helen's face lit up with genuine pleasure.

"Sweetheart!" she cried, "where have you been?" There was unmistakable warmth beneath the flirtatious scolding that accompanied the pouring of her soup. "I've been worried about you. How could you pass up my homemade soup last weekend?"

Helen actually makes several gallons of soup herself in her own home each Friday. It's the real thing—as is Helen's personal concern for her "sweethearts."

Love and the hope of it are not things one can learn; they are part of life's heritage.
MARIA MONTESSORI

God doesn't look at how much we do, but with how much love we do it.
MOTHER TERESA

The best things come in small packages.
FRENCH PROVERB

If I bestow all my goods to feed the poor... but do not have love, it does me no good.
THE BIBLE (1 COR. 13:3)

You can give without loving, but you can't love without giving.
OSWALD J. SMITH

THEMES
■ COMPASSION ■ KINDNESS ■ LOVE
■ SIMPLICITY ■ CHARITY

Off The Planet

On the New Year's Eve that ushered in 1992, the great bells of Moscow rang out to signal the end of the Soviet Union and the beginning of the new Commonwealth of Independent States. Seven months before, a cosmonaut named Sergei Krikalyov had begun a mission aboard the Soviet space station *Mir*.

When he blasted off from the Baikonur cosmodrome, Krikalyov knew what he was and where he was from: he was a card-carrying member of the Communist Party and he was from Kazakhistan in the Soviet Union. His spacecraft proudly bore the hammer and sickle and his helmet was engraved with the initials that stood for his country: USSR.

He was orbiting at incredible speeds in the world of space, a world more familiar to Sergei than the one he had left behind. For now his Communist card, which had always been the only ticket to advancement, made him a member of an illegal organization. As a Soviet citizen, he was a foreigner from a non-existent country as far as the new state of Kazakhistan was concerned.

The world from which he had blasted off was gone forever. Enormous changes that rarely take place in one person's lifetime occurred in just seven months for Sergei Krikalyov—and he wasn't even on the planet! He of all people surely could say, "Look what happened when I turned my back!"

Change is the constant, the signal for rebirth, the egg of the phoenix.
CHRISTINA BALDWIN

People change and forget to tell each other.
LILLIAN HELLMAN

With each new day I put away the past and discover the new beginnings I have been given.
ANGELA L. WOZNIAK

The reasonable man adapts himself to the world; the unreasonable one persists in trying to adapt the world to himself. Therefore all progress depends on the unreasonable man.
GEORGE BERNARD SHAW

THEMES
■ CHANGE ■ ADAPTABILITY
■ PROGRESS ■ DISCOVERY

Two Notes

Samuel Clemens, better known as Mark Twain, told many tall tales, true "whoppers" in his books. And many of them were based on incidents in Twain's own very colorful life. One such story appears in *Roughing It*. Here is how it happened in real life:

Clemens and his partner Calvin Higbie stumbled onto a million-dollar silver mine. They staked a claim for it at once. The legislation covering such claims required that the mine be worked for an initial ten-day period by the claimants. At the end of that period, the ore was theirs.

Apparently neither Mr Clemens nor Mr Higbie liked hard work. Higbie left a note for Clemens to the effect that he could not work the mine because he had to go to California, so Clemens should start digging.

Along comes Clemens with a note of his own. He is so preoccupied with his plan that he fails to see Higbie's note. The note

Clemens leaves says that he has gone to take care of a sick friend and would be away for days (so Higbie should start digging!).

Neither Higbie nor Clemens returned to the mine until several days after the claim period had expired. By then it was too late. All they could do was stand sadly by and watch others work the precious ore.

Continuous effort—not strength or intelligence—is the key to unlocking our potential.
LIANE CORDES

Experience is a good teacher, but she sends in terrific bills.
MINNA ANTRIM

The force, the mass of character, mind, heart or soul that a man can put into any work, is the most important factor in that work.
A. P. PEABODY

I like work; it fascinates me. I can sit and look at it for hours. I love to keep it by me; the idea of getting rid of it nearly breaks my heart.
JEROME K. JEROME

THEMES
■ LAZINESS ■ DECEPTION ■ GREED
■ LABOR ■ COOPERATION
■ EFFORT ■ WORK

The Thousand Poems

Vo Dai Ton spent ten years in a Vietnamese prison without any contact with the outside world. His cell had no running water and no toilet facilities. His hands and legs were chained and a rope was tied around his neck. Twice a month he was beaten unconscious.

A former colonel of the Republic of Vietnam, Ton had left his wife, Tuyet Mai, and his three-year-old son Paul in Australia in 1980 and had gone back to Vietnam to join in an attempt to overthrow the communists. Captured, he had been jailed with no trial and then beaten regularly for forty-five days. But it was isolation in his 2.5 by 3-metre cell for ten long years that was the worst torture.

"They tried breaking my spirit," he said after his release and return to Australia in 1991, "but they could not. The spirit of survival kept me going."

Vo Dai Ton's method of survival was most unique. He was a soldier but he was also a poet. He kept sane through the ten years of prison hell by writing—only in his mind—some one thousand poems! These he painstakingly committed to memory, together with the outline and content for three books!

After the joyful reunion with his family, Ton began the task of committing to paper the thousand poems and the three books. If circumstances of composition have anything to do with the final result of a work, then Ton's writing must be of the highest quality.

Regardless of their literary value, these works are a monument to the resilience of the human spirit.

All sorts of spiritual gifts come through privation, if they are accepted.
JANET ERSKINE STUART

Poetry is life distilled.
GWENDOLYN BROOKS

Stone walls do not a Prison make
Nor Iron bars a Cage;
Minds innocent and quiet take
That for an hermitage.
RICHARD LOVELACE

THEMES
▪ PRIVATION ▪ POETRY ▪ FREEDOM
▪ PRISON ▪ COURAGE ▪ WILL TO LIVE
▪ SPIRIT ▪ SUFFERING

The Hardest Job

Famous Australian film director Bruce Beresford has met many challenges during his celebrated career. The acclaimed movie, *Black Robe*, posed its own set of challenges. The first ever coproduction between Canada and Australia, the film had to present authentically the historical period in which French Jesuit missionaries braved the New World to work among the Indians of Quebec.

"Period films are always hard to do," said Beresford. "The further back in history you go, the harder it is."

Black Robe was also a logistics nightmare because the weather in the Saguenay-Lac St Jean region of Northern Quebec is bitterly cold in winter. Lothaire Bluteau, the lead actor who plays the part of the over-zealous missionary, Fr Laforgue, ended up with a frozen jaw.

But Beresford's greatest challenge as the director of *Black Robe* was probably not the weather nor accuracy of historical portrayal.

It was in making the priest's obsession believable to film-goers today.

Beresford put it this way in an interview: "He had an obsession with getting people into heaven. This is a concept few people these days take seriously. My job was to convince an audience that this is important."

Said with tongue in cheek?

Zeal is the faculty igniting the other mind powers into the full flame of activity.
SYLVIA STITT EDWARDS

There aren't any good, brave causes left. If the big bang does come, and we all get killed off, it won't be in aid of the old-fashioned design. It'll just be for the Brave New-nothing-very-much-thank-you.
JOHN OSBORNE,
IN *LOOK BACK IN ANGER*

Earth's crammed with heaven,
And every common bush afire with God.
ELIZABETH BARRETT BROWNING

THEMES
▪ HEAVEN ▪ FILMS ▪ CHALLENGE
▪ MISSIONARIES ▪ PRIESTS ▪ ZEAL

Just Put My Name

....

On 10 January 1864 in the Bowery, New York City's infamous street of drunken doorway dwellers, a flophouse inhabitant lay unconscious and bleeding on the common bathroom floor. Three days later, Friday the 13th, he died penniless among the destitute in Bellevue Hospital, with no family near.

That tragic alcoholic was Stephen Foster, the composer of such famous songs as "Swanee River," "Oh Susannah," and "I Dream of Jeannie with the Light Brown Hair." Born to a prosperous family, he was the only son who did not become a successful businessman. He went to an academy but left after two years. He went to a college but left after a few months. He talked of joining the Navy but never did. He joined his brother Dunning's company as a bookkeeper but at his desk he secretly composed music and hid the sheets between the pages of the ledgers. Needless to say, he left that job after only a couple of years.

Stephen Foster married but that did not last either.

Yet today this "failure" is known the world over. His hit, "Swanee River," is second only to "La Marseillaise" in international fame. Even in his lifetime his songs were selling extremely well and reaping enormous profits for everyone involved except poor Foster.

For any song Stephen usually received about $10! He even got only this pittance in exchange for the exclusive rights to "Swanee"! Music publishers constantly cheated him, knowing that in his destitution and longing for a drink he would accept a few dollars for his great works.

The tragedy of Stephen Foster could be said to have begun in childhood when his father refused to recognise his musical talent and kept trying to push him into what he, the elder Foster, considered to be important careers.

A great thirst for recognition haunted Stephen all his life. No incident makes that clearer than his pathetic request to E. L. Christy, who published 400,000 copies of "Swanee River" under his own name, rather than Foster's. "I'll give you back the $10 you paid me," Stephen pleaded, "if you'll just put my name on the song."

O God! that men should put an enemy in their
mouths to steal away their brains.
WILLIAM SHAKESPEARE, *OTHELLO*

Everyone pushes a falling fence.
CHINESE PROVERB

The less choice you have,
the poorer you are.
CARRIE SAXON PERRY

Alcohol doesn't console, it doesn't fill up anyone's
psychological gaps; all it replaces is the lack of God.
MARGUERITE DURAS

THEMES
■ DESPAIR ■ ADDICTION ■ FAME
■ ALCOHOL ■ FAILURE
■ CAREER ■ POVERTY

Good Deeds?

Two Boy Scouts approached a crosswalk at the same time as an old woman laden with shopping bags. Ahead of them, almost on the other side of the street, a young boy was helping a crippled man make a safe crossing.

"That bloody Matthew!" one of the Scouts spluttered. "How'd he beat me to it? I had figured I'd use old Mr Jenkins for my good deed for the day!"

"You!" the other snapped. "I had him in my sights first!"

In anger and disgust the two stomped off. The old lady at the crosswalk shifted her parcels, sighed wearily, and struggled on.

Nothing is so irretrievably missed as a daily opportunity.
MARIE VON EBNER-ESCHENBACH

Take egotism out, and you would castrate the benefactors.
RALPH WALDO EMERSON

There is a haphazard sort of doing good, which is
nothing but temperamental pleasure-seeking.
FANNY LEWALD

THEMES
■ OPPORTUNITY ■ GOODNESS
■ HELP ■ KINDNESS

Not Me!
(sequel to "Good Deeds?")

Matthew and Mr Jenkins stepped onto the curb. "Thank you, my lad," murmured the crippled man, and he moved off.

Meanwhile another old man crossing behind them approached Matthew. "It's so nice to see a young fellow doing his good deed for the day!" he boomed heartily, clapping a bony hand on Matt's shoulder.

Matthew wriggled uncomfortably. "Good deed?" he repeated in surprise. "Not me, Mister, I was just helping someone cross the street."

The best exercise for the heart is to lean over backwards for somebody else.
ANONYMOUS

He who would do good to another must do it in minute particulars.
WILLIAM BLAKE

One of the deep secrets of life is that all that is really worth the doing is what we do for others.
LEWIS CARROLL

THEMES
▪ GOODNESS ▪ HELP
▪ KINDNESS ▪ ATTITUDE

Parachuting Grandma

A woman gave her mother a most unusual birthday gift: she paid for parachuting lessons. So after proper preparation at the Moree Parachuting Club, Mrs Sally Rail found herself in a plane with her instructor, about to take her first jump. Unlike most first jumpers, she felt no fear as the plane climbed to 10,000 feet.

"When you've wanted to do something for 50 years," she said, her face glowing, "you're not going to be frightened at the last moment!"

Yes, Sally was 77 on that first jump, a grandmother with severe arthritis in both legs. In her long life she had had many adventures, such as shooting a leopard at close range in Rhodesia, rally car driving in West Africa, obtaining her own pilot's license in South Africa, whitewater-rafting in New Zealand, abseiling in Queensland—to name a few...

Sally described the reaction to her latest adventure: "All my friends, including people much younger than me, looked at me as if I was mad." She said she intended to go again, but "much higher, so I can free-fall for longer."

It was the free-falling that most captured Sally's thrill-loving heart: "I lost all sense of time and there was this huge roar of wind rushing past my ears. I felt I didn't belong anywhere. It was just so wonderful!"

The most impressive thing about Sally Rail was the zest for life so evident in the press coverage of her jump. Why get bored or old or both when you can fall through the air at 10,000 feet and derive from it "an indescribable feeling of elation"? Who knows what else life may hold when one can fall freely without fear?

Zest is the secret of all beauty. There is no beauty that is attractive without zest.
CHRISTIAN DIOR

*Be a new and different person, with a fresh newness
in all you do and think.*
THE BIBLE (ROMANS 12:22)

*I want to feel myself part of things, of the great
drift and swirl—not cut off, missings things, like
being sent to bed early as a child.*
JOANNA FIELD

THEMES
■ FEAR ■ ZEST ■ ADVENTURE
■ ELDERLY ■ WILL TO LIVE ■ ATTITUDE

One At A Time

Perth doctor Ken Collins has served the poor in India, the Philippines, Mauritius and Indonesia, as well as refugees in Hong Kong and Papua New Guinea. He has seen the severest poverty and fought disease in one depressed area after another.

It was not unusual for him to treat as many as one hundred and fifty patients a day. In the Straits of Malacca he sailed up and down in an old fishing boat which he had made into a dispensary, treating fishermen and their families, in 30°C heat, from eight in the morning until ten at night.

As with so many who try to alleviate poverty and sickness in specific areas—in one village here or one neighborhood there—Dr Collins has faced the query: "Does it really do any lasting good? For every few you help there are hundreds of thousands more you can't reach." The answer comes in the form of a parable:

"It's like the story of a guy walking along the beach. Hundreds of starfish are shrivelling in the heat. He comes across a man throwing the fish, one at a time, back into the sea. 'Hey,' he yells, 'what good do you think you're doing when there are hundreds of fish dying?'

"The man picks up a fish and replies, 'For this little bloke here, mate, it means a lot,' and he tosses it back into the water."

I have always depended on the kindness of strangers.
TENNESSEE WILLIAMS,
IN *A STREETCAR NAMED DESIRE*

Ah, but a man's reach should exceed his grasp
Or what's a heaven for?
ROBERT BROWNING

Concern should drive us into action
and not into depression.
KAREN HORNEY

THEMES
▪ HELP ▪ GOODNESS ▪ KINDNESS
▪ ATTITUDE ▪ POVERTY

The Protector

The young priest came upon the boy lying in his vomit, cold and agonising from heroin withdrawal. Compassionately but without overkill—this priest had some thirteen years of experience helping Sydney's street kids—he asked, "You've been really sick, but how are you feeling now?"

"I've been off the stuff five days, Father," was the reply, "and I'm not half as bad today as I was yesterday." No heroics, no self-pity, just a surprisingly positive answer.

"Let me take you out of here," the priest urged. He knew this kid wouldn't come back to the refuge. The most he could hope for was that he might accept some hot food, blankets, and a lift back to the abandoned, rat-infested garage he called home. At least it was warmer and drier than the streets that particular night.

The boy started to refuse the offer. Then, seeing two tough-looking characters running up to ask for a lift, he got into the ute and crawled under a tarpaulin. The two newcomers wanted a ride to Central Station, so the priest drove them there. They never noticed the first kid under the tarpaulin.

"You can let me out here, too," the sick boy said after the other two had hopped out.

"But why did you come with us if you weren't intending to go to your squat?" queried the puzzled priest.

"Father, you did a really stupid thing tonight," came the quiet reply. "You took two total strangers into your ute—they could have pulled a knife on you or bashed you up. I had to come along in case they tried anything."

He shuffled off, leaving behind a very moved helper.

Love is either the shrinking remnant of something which was once enormous; or else it is part of something which will grow in the future into something enormous.

ANTON CHEKHOV

Serve one another in love.

THE BIBLE (GAL. 5:13)

There are as many ways to live and grow as there are people.

EVELYN MANDEL

THEMES
■ HELP ■ GOODNESS ■ PRUDENCE
■ KINDNESS ■ COMPASSION ■ DRUGS

Hidden Message

The child was from a very wealthy home and had been given just about everything a little girl could desire. Yet when the preschool teacher met with the parents, she had to report that little Michelle always seemed unhappy, or at best, quiet and withdrawn. Could Mum and Dad suggest any explanation or did they have any suggestions that might be tried out in the preschool?

No, both parents said they could not think of any reason for the apparent sadness nor did they have any idea what to do.

Was she happy at home? Yes, everything seemed fine. The teacher's face showed her bewilderment as the interview ended.

In the weeks that followed, Michelle gave no clue as to her evident distress. "I'm okay, thank you," she would always reply politely. "I like it here a lot." But her caring teacher knew she needed help. Yet what kind of help? For what?

The answer came unexpectedly one day in a drawing session. The children were asked to draw their own homes. Michelle was doing quite a good representation of her family mansion when the teacher reached her desk. "That's good, Michelle," she said, and was about to walk on when she suddenly realised that the house showed no windows. In fact, there was no door either.

"Why haven't you drawn any windows and doors?" she asked.

Without a moment's pause, Michelle replied firmly, "That's so Daddy can't get in!"

Cries for help come in an infinite variety of ways.

So long as little children are allowed to suffer,
there is no true love in this world.
ISADORA DUNCAN

Weak men are apt to be cruel.
GEORGE SAVILLE

Actions speak louder than words.
AMERICAN PROVERB

THEMES
■ ABUSE (CHILD) ■ UNHAPPINESS
■ CHILDREN ■ PARENTS ■ FAMILY
■ FEAR ■ COMMUNICATION

Rent-A-Family

What do you do when you're a grandparent whose children and grandchildren don't come to see you much any more? If you feel overcome by loneliness and sadness?

A Japanese entrepreneur realised that his country had a great number in this situation and decided to offer a service that would bring relief by fantasy.

For the staggering sum of 150,000 yen, his company, NKH, will provide three trained "stand-in family members" for a three-hour period. Does he get clients easily? He certainly does—and always has a good number on his waiting list!

"Rent-a-family" works like this: The hired actors play the roles of children, grandchildren, daughters and sons-in-law—whatever the clients require. Normally, says NKH president Karoru Inoue, they just sit around and talk, but often the clients berate their "pretend" children for leaving them so alone and sad.

Why has this unusual scheme caught on? Mr Inoue's convinced reply is an indictment of our inhuman society: "There are lots of old people who feel sad because everyone is chasing money and no one is paying attention to the human spirit."

The debt of gratitude we owe our mother and father
goes forward, not backward.
NANCY FRIDAY

Children aren't happy with nothing to ignore
And that's what parents are created for.
OGDEN NASH

Charity begins at home.
ENGLISH PROVERB

THEMES
■ FAMILY ■ CHILDREN ■ NEGLECT
■ PARENTS ■ ELDERLY ■ INGRATITUDE

Memories

Helen was a highly competent executive and an excellent manager. When the personnel department of her large company suggested she and her staff attend a half-day workshop on building team spirit, she readily assented.

The session began with the facilitator asking each person to talk a bit about his or her childhood as part of the "getting-to-know-each-other-better" goal. Before speaking, all were to take a few minutes to immerse themselves back into the reality of those long-ago years.

When her turn came, Helen launched easily into an account of her early family life and spoke with pride of her schoolteacher mother who was so well liked that students often came to their home to seek her advice and help.

Then it happened. To the utter astonishment of the group—and Helen herself more surprised than anyone—she broke into great gasping sobs. Try as she might, she could not seem to stop. Finally she managed to utter an embarrassed apology prior to going on with her story—only to find herself weeping brokenly again. The words that came out between the wrenching sobs were: "Mother had time for all the kids, but not for me. I used to watch them coming and talking with her and I'd wish she would sit and listen to me like that. But she never did."

In the stillness that followed, Helen added softly, "And until now I never knew that my pain was still so strong. I haven't thought of it for years. But the hurt has been buried down there all this time."

We tend to think of the rational as a higher order, but it is the emotional that marks our lives.
MERLE SHAIN

Now that I'm in my forties, she [mother] sends me presents, and we have the long, personal and even remarkably honest phone calls I always wanted so intensely I forbade myself to imagine them. How strange.
MARGE PIERCY

Is there any stab as deep as wondering where and how you failed those you loved?
FLORIDA SCOTT-MAXWELL

THEMES
■ MOTHERS ■ NEGLECT
■ PARENTS ■ PAIN

Mew?

What do you do when you live alone in one of the millions of flats that are home to city dwellers the world over? You'd like a dog or cat to keep you company, or warn off intruders, but in most places such pets are not allowed.

It is an enterprising Japanese company that has come up with a solution. It markets "Mew", an electronic cat that will purr when stroked, thanks to a sensor. Of course, your purring companion is priced like a true pedigreed feline!

A competitor offers "Super Doggy Guard One", a mechanical dog that barks when anything moves, thanks to its high-tech sensor. Still another rival on the Japanese market is a toy pup with an advanced voice-recognition device. The pup responds to its owner's voice with a bark and a wag of its tail.

Admirable though these commercial ventures may be, one wonders if the successful marketing of "Mew", "Super Doggy" and "His Master's Pup" says something about modern urban living...

I hate to go to bed, I hate to get up,
and I hate to be alone.
TALLULAH BANKHEAD

Loneliness and the feeling of being unwanted
is the most terrible poverty.
MOTHER TERESA

At any moment, solitude may put
on the face of loneliness.
MAY SARTON

*I had three chairs in my house: one for solitude,
two for friendship, three for society.*

HENRY DAVID THOREAU

THEMES
▪ LONELINESS ▪ PETS
▪ COMPANIONSHIP

Highway Panic

A young woman had a long drive ahead of her that night. She pulled into a service station to refuel, then went inside to pay and buy herself some gum and potato chips. As she drove off, a huge truck pulled out behind her.

Out on the highway once again, the girl realised that the truck was very close behind, uncomfortably close! She stepped on the accelerator, but to her dismay, the truck driver accelerated too.

"I must be imagining this," she thought, trying not to panic. Yet whether she slowed down, changed lanes or speeded up, the truck stayed with her, its big headlights shining straight into her car.

Unable to stand it any longer, the girl turned into the next station she came to. The truck pulled off the highway right on her tail. Jamming on the brakes, she jumped out and raced to the driver's side of the truck. At the same moment, a man leapt out of the back of her car where he had been crouching ever since the last stop. The truck driver was too quick for him and caught him just as he tried to make it to the open field behind the station.

Later, after the police had come, the driver went over to the young woman. "I saw him jump into your car just before you came out of the station back there, but there was no time to warn you before you drove off. The only thing I could think of was to stick so close to you with my high beams flooding your car so that he'd know I'd see him if he tried to do anything to you."

All she could say, with a mighty sigh of relief, was, "And here I was wondering how I was going to shake off a crazed truck driver!"

The hands that help are holier than the lips that pray.
R. G. INGERSOLL

*Acceptance is... acknowledgement of the facts of a situation.
Then deciding what you're going to do about it*
KATHLEEN CASEY THEISEN

*My doctrine is this, that if we see cruelty or wrong
that we have the power to stop, and do nothing, we make
ourselves sharers in the guilt.*
ANNA SEWELL

THEMES
■ HELP ■ GOODNESS ■ ACTION
■ KINDNESS ■ FEAR

Gut Feelings

....

"I always get a gut feeling when I have to make a choice, and that's what I follow," said the first lady.

"Oh, and does it always come out right?"

"Yes, but sometimes it takes me a while to get in touch with my deepest self."

Her friend was very impressed by all this terminology. "I don't know about gut feelings and all," she began hesitantly, "but I do remember a time when I knew instantly what choice to make."

"Tell me about it," urged the pop psychologist, intrigued.

"Well, I was holidaying in a town when I fell very ill. They asked me which doctor I wanted. I didn't know anyone of course but when they told me who was available, it wasn't hard to make up my mind. The two doctors were called Dr Allwright and Dr Croaker!"

The best doctors in the world are Doctor Diet,
Doctor Quiet and Doctor Merryman.
JONATHAN SWIFT

What I call a good patient is one who, having found
a good physician, sticks to him till he dies.
OLIVER WENDELL HOLMES

Trusting our intuition often saves us from disaster.
ANNE WILSON SCHAEF

THEMES
■ FEELINGS ■ INTUITION
■ PSYCHOLOGY ■ CHOICE
■ DOCTORS ■ ILLNESS

What Do You Say?

What do you say when you finish a major enterprise?

Pious people often exclaim: "Praise the Lord!"

Alexander Graham Bell's first message over his newly invented telegraph was, "What hath God wrought!"

But according to medieval Cabalist literature, when the creation of the world was finished, God exclaimed, "Let's hope it works!"

More than anything else, God loves admiration . . . I think it pisses God off if you walk by the color purple in a field somewhere and don't notice it.

ALICE WALKER, *THE COLOR PURPLE*

The world is charged with the grandeur of God.

GERALD MANLEY HOPKINS

If the Lord Almighty had consulted me before embarking upon Creation, I should have recommended something simpler.

ALFONSO X

THEMES
■ **PRAISE** ■ **GOD**
■ **CREATION** ■ **HOPE**

Prague's Window Washer

In 1978 Miloslav Vik began a new career. He became a window washer of Prague's government buildings. He must have done quite well on the job, for he held the post for ten years.

Officials looking out their clean windows would have had no idea that the competent washer was a priest. Having had his priestly license revoked by the Communist authorities, Fr Miloslav had found another way to earn a living.

The Communist government is gone now, and so is the window washer. Miloslav Vik not only returned to full-time ministry—he became Archbishop of that very same city of Prague!

In an interview granted to the diocesan newspaper of Dallas, *The Texas Catholic*, the Archbishop revealed the attitude that sustained him through it all: "The will of God can be different in different moments of our life. Sometimes it is His will that I be a window washer, and at other times, Archbishop."

There's a divinity that shapes our ends,
Rough-hew them how we will.
WILLIAM SHAKESPEARE, *HAMLET*

Nothing splendid has ever been achieved except by
those who dared to believe that something inside them
was superior to circumstance.
BRUCE BARTON

We have to become as simple and as wordless
as the growing corn or the falling rain.
We must just be.
ETTY HILLESUM

In the midst of winter I finally learned that there was in me an invincible summer.

A. CAMUS

THEMES
▪ ACCEPTANCE ▪ OPTIMISM
▪ ATTITUDE ▪ SIMPLICITY
▪ CAREER ▪ HOPE
▪ GOD ▪ ACHIEVEMENT

Short-Changed

The little boy wrote to Santa with a desperate plea: could Santa please send $500 right away because Mum and him and the other kids need it badly.

The letter addressed to Santa arrived at the post office of the small town and was passed on to a local charity known as the Helpers. Without waiting for the next meeting or an organized appeal, several of the members pooled their resources and got a $300 cheque off to the boy. They accompanied the cheque with a little note signed "Santa's Helpers."

A week later, another letter for Santa arrived at the post office: "Dear Santa, thank you very much for answering so quickly. That was great! Your friend, Tom.

"(PS Next time could you send it straight to me—those Helpers of yours take a big commission!)"

Trust everybody—but cut the cards.
FINLEY PETER DUNNE

Children awaken your own sense of self when you see them hurting, struggling, testing; when you watch their eyes and listen to their hearts. Children are gifts, if we accept them.
KATHLEEN TIERNEY CRILLY

Time, self-pity, apathy, bitterness and exhaustion can take the Christmas out of the child, but cannot take the child out of Christmas.

ERMA BOMBECK

THEMES
■ HELP ■ CHRISTMAS
■ SIMPLICITY ■ TRUST
■ CHILDREN

The Target

···

When Michael Aris married Aung San Suu Kyi in 1972, this distinguished Oxford professor was not only marrying the beautiful daughter of Burma's assassinated General Aung San, he was marrying a patriot who warned him that one day her country might require her service.

In April of 1988, after sixteen years of marriage and motherhood, Suu travelled to Burma to be with her dying mother. But she could never be just a private citizen visiting home again, for at that moment the country was torn with mass demonstrations against the military regime, and was she not the daughter of Burma's greatest nationalist hero?

Before long, Suu had turned the rioting mobs into a disciplined political force, with non-violent principles, fighting for basic human rights. A devout Buddhist, Suu wanted to be another Gandhi uniting all factions in her tormented country. But the military, to whom she extended the hand of peace and collaboration, rejected her and refused to relinquish power even when her party won an overwhelming victory.

In 1991, Aung San Suu Kyi, scholar, wife, mother and advocate of freedom and democracy, won the Nobel Peace Prize—but could not be there in person to accept it because she was under house arrest.

Over and over Suu has spoken out against apathy and fear, and her incredible experiences, such as the following, give us some idea about what it means to be free of fear.

One day while out campaigning with members of her party, Suu was suddenly faced with a squad of soldiers who leapt out of a jeep and prepared to fire. She gestured to her coworkers to move out of the way and then, alone, walked straight toward the guns. Down the middle of that street she walked, without flinching, never taking her eyes off the faces of the soldiers.

"Withdraw!" barked the squad commander, and the terrible moment was over.

"It seemed so much simpler to provide them with a single target," Suu said later, "than to bring all the others in."

*I long to speak out the intense inspiration that comes
to me from lives of strong women.*
RUTH BENEDICT

*You don't get to choose how you're going to die. Or when.
You can only decide how you're going to live. Now.*
JOAN BAEZ

*You only have power over people so long as
you don't take everything away from them. But when you've
robbed a man of everything, he's no longer in your power
—he's free again.*
ALEXANDER SOLZHENITSYN

*Such is the patriot's boast, where'er we roam,
His first, best country ever is, at home.*
OLIVER GOLDSMITH

THEMES
▪ COURAGE ▪ CONFLICT ▪ FREEDOM
▪ JUSTICE ▪ CIVIL RIGHTS ▪ ACTION
▪ DEATH ▪ PATRIOTISM
▪ POWER ▪ FEAR

Point of View

Everyone felt that the final choice of the host city of the Olympic Games in the year 2000 would be a close race. Some predicted a one- or two-vote margin.

In Australia, the countdown to the announcement saw emotions running high. While outwardly expressing confidence that Sydney would be chosen, many were prepared for the worst. Beijing was a very strong contender.

It seemed that during those suspenseful final days, the traditional rivalry between Sydney and Melbourne had been put on hold. After all, wouldn't a win for Sydney be a huge plus for the whole country?...

But after the waiting world had been told that Sydney's bid had indeed been successful, and after the first wave of euphoria had passed over Sydney, it was revealed that a Melbourne newspaper had had two front-page headlines in readiness. Depending on the outcome of the International Olympic Committee vote, the paper was to trumpet:

WE'VE WON!

or

SYDNEY LOST.

In great cities where people of ability abound, there is always a feverish urge to keep ahead, to set the pace...
CHARLOTTE PERKINS GILMAN

We throw all our attention on the utterly idle question whether A has done as well as B, when the only question is whether A has done as well as he could.
WILLIAM G. SUMNER

*Doctors bury their mistakes. Lawyers hang them. But
journalists put theirs on the front page.*
ANONYMOUS

THEMES
▪ RIVALRY ▪ ATTITUDE
▪ CITIES ▪ NEWSPAPERS

Leaving His Mark

Federico Fellini left an indelible mark on film-making with his pungent satire on modern society. More particularly, he had a genius for portraying the loneliness of men and women today.

So distinct was his style that people began describing it with the new word, "felliniesque."

"My father wanted me to become an engineer," said Fellini, reminiscing. "My mother wanted me to be a bishop. But me? I'm quite happy to have become an adjective!"

It is a peaceful thing to be succeeding.
GERTRUDE STEIN

The happy people are failures because they are on such good terms with themselves that they don't give a damn.
AGATHA CHRISTIE

Every lot is happy if you are content with it.
BOETHIUS

Success to me is having 10 honeydew melons and eating only the top half of each one.
BARBRA STREISAND

THEMES
■ ATTITUDE ■ AMBITION
■ CAREER ■ SUCCESS
■ CONTENTMENT ■ HAPPINESS